The Open Ur.

T357
Structural integrity:
designing against failure

BLOCK 2
FRACTURE MECHANICS

PART 1: PRACTICAL
FRACTURE MECHANICS
PART 2: FATIGUE

This publication forms part of an Open University course T357 *Structural integrity: designing against failure*. Details of this and other Open University courses can be obtained from the Student Registration and Enquiry Service, The Open University, PO Box 197, Milton Keynes MK7 6BJ, United Kingdom: tel. +44 (0)845 300 60 90, email general-enquiries@open.ac.uk

Alternatively, you may visit the Open University website at http://www.open.ac.uk where you can learn more about the wide range of courses and packs offered at all levels by The Open University.

To purchase a selection of Open University course materials visit http://www.ouw.co.uk, or contact Open University Worldwide, Walton Hall, Milton Keynes MK7 6AA, United Kingdom for a brochure. tel. +44 (0)1908 858793; fax +44 (0)1908 858787; email ouw-customer-services@open.ac.uk

The Open University
Walton Hall, Milton Keynes
MK7 6AA

First published 2007. Second edition 2009.

Edited and designed by The Open University.

Typeset by SR Nova Pvt. Ltd, Bangalore, India.

Printed and bound in the United Kingdom by Latimer Trend & Company Ltd, Plymouth.

ISBN 978 0 7492 5270 0

2.1

FSC
www.fsc.org
MIX
Paper from
responsible sources
FSC® C013436

The paper used in this publication contains pulp sourced from forests independently certified to the Forest Stewardship Council (FSC) principles and criteria. Chain of custody certification allows the pulp from these forests to be tracked to the end use (see www.fsc.org).

CONTENTS

INTRODUCTION TO BLOCK 2   3

PART 1 PRACTICAL FRACTURE MECHANICS   7

   1   Introduction   11

   2   Linear-elastic fracture mechanics   16

   3   Linear-elastic fracture mechanics in practice   38

   4   Summary   48

   Learning outcomes   49

   Answers to exercises   50

   Answers to self-assessment questions   55

   Acknowledgements   59

PART 2 FATIGUE   **61**

   1   Introduction   65

   2   Fatigue behaviour of materials   76

   3   Using fatigue data in design   92

   4   Applying fracture mechanics to fatigue   101

   5   A practical example: the Markham disaster   123

   6   Summary: fatigue design   125

   Learning outcomes   126

   Answers to exercises   127

   Answers to self-assessment questions   130

   References   136

   Acknowledgements   137

INTRODUCTION TO BLOCK 2

INTRODUCTION TO BLOCK 2

Block 1 introduced you to stress analysis: determining and quantifying the stress in components and structures. Block 2 is about how we design parts knowing that they may contain flaws, or may develop flaws in service from wear, fatigue or degradation.

Ideally, once a component or structure has been fabricated, we would like it to have an infinite life and never need to be maintained. In reality, this is unattainable: cost constraints in manufacture, limits to materials properties, fundamental physical limits and the need for pragmatic engineering mean that manufactured objects do not last for ever. Components wear and corrode, and structures such as aircraft suffer from fatigue cracking. Some products will contain flaws or cracks from the moment of their construction; and, although this may be an unwanted state of affairs, it's something that needs to be understood and accounted for in design. Cracks in materials can, as you might expect, cause failures to occur at significantly lower applied loads than would otherwise be the case.

Part 1 of this block introduces you to the application of the theory of fracture mechanics to engineering parts, primarily made from metals, that contain cracks or flaws. I shall cover different industrial sectors, from nuclear reactors to aeroplanes, where the theories are applied in different ways according to the types of structure and the way that they are used. I will address the practical aspects of applying theories concerned with the behaviour of cracked bodies, and provide an appreciation of the underlying fundamentals that inform those theories: hence the title of 'Practical fracture mechanics'.

Part 2 looks in detail at the phenomenon of fatigue, where cracks can initiate and then grow in a material even in the absence of an obvious initial flaw. The consideration of fatigue loading is a critical part of the design process, as the progression from a pristine component to a broken one can be surprisingly rapid under certain loading conditions.

Part 3 looks at *how* materials fail on the microscale, and how a structure can resist the development of cracks and damage.

Part 4 covers the very important topic of degradation in service. Key to the success of any product is that it is able to survive the conditions in which it operates, and very few materials are entirely resistant to attack from the elements – not everything can be made from gold …

Part 5 looks at an extension of fracture mechanics to cases where significant plasticity may be associated with the growth of a crack in a material, and how assessments of possible failures are performed in such cases.

Finally, in Part 6, the block ends with some case studies exemplifying the concepts that you have met throughout this course.

Associated with this block are three calculators, written in Microsoft® Excel, which are provided on the course DVD to save you the labour of repetitive calculations: the 'K calculator', the 'Fatigue calculator' and the 'R6 calculator'. In the first part of this block you will learn to perform the calculations longhand and then gain some acquaintance with the K calculator. Later on in your studies, the use of the calculators takes over. The calculators are to aid teaching of the engineering, so that the important teaching points are not overwhelmed by repetitive sums. You will be able to use the calculators to answer continuous-assessment questions, but you will not have the calculators in the exam room, so try not to anticipate the use of the calculators to do the exercises that are set longhand.

PART 1
PRACTICAL FRACTURE MECHANICS

CONTENTS

1	**INTRODUCTION**	**11**
1.1	Introduction to fracture mechanics	11
1.2	Materials properties and testing	13
1.3	The story so far	15
2	**LINEAR-ELASTIC FRACTURE MECHANICS**	**16**
2.1	Brittle and ductile fracture	16
2.2	The linear-elastic fracture mechanics equation	17
2.3	The parameters of linear-elastic fracture mechanics	22
	2.3.1 Fracture toughness K_{IC}	22
	2.3.2 Geometrical factor Y	29
	2.3.3 Far-field stress σ	32
	2.3.4 Crack length	35
	2.3.5 Review of the parameters	36
3	**LINEAR-ELASTIC FRACTURE MECHANICS IN PRACTICE**	**38**
3.1	Applying fracture mechanics	42
3.2	Plastic collapse	45
4	**SUMMARY**	**48**
	LEARNING OUTCOMES	**49**
	ANSWERS TO EXERCISES	**50**
	ANSWERS TO SELF-ASSESSMENT QUESTIONS	**55**
	ACKNOWLEDGEMENTS	**59**

1 INTRODUCTION

1.1 Introduction to fracture mechanics

Fracture mechanics is the study of cracked structures under load. Engineers now routinely buy and run plant and machinery that is cracked, whereas once the idea that a bought and paid-for piece of equipment might contain cracks was unacceptable. George Irwin, the founder of modern fracture mechanics, said that in the 1940s 'it was not considered mannerly to talk about cracks in newly fabricated structures'.

The presence of cracks in safety-critical structures is inevitable, particularly when they are fabricated by welding. This means that high-pressure gas pipelines in suburban areas, nuclear pressure vessels (usually a little further away from major population centres), and chemical plant containing dangerous substances are commissioned and used cracked. Despite this, failures under static load are rare nowadays. There are two major reasons for this: metals are now much 'cleaner' (containing fewer flaws), have very good properties and are well characterized, and the safety of critical structures is assured by ☑ **proof testing** ☑.

☑ Proof testing

Proof testing is a technique whereby components that are not up to specification can be identified before entering service. The usual principle employed is to expose the components briefly to conditions more severe than they would be expected to endure in service. A badly flawed component is likely to be destroyed by a proof test, so it is not undertaken lightly. Clearly a failure during proof testing is less harmful than an unexpected failure in service. One important assumption of this approach is that exposure to the more severe conditions during proof testing does not in itself damage the component.

Proof testing is often used on safety-critical components that may contain flaws or defects and are relatively highly stressed in service. For example, ceramic grinding wheels are exposed to large stresses as they are spun at high speed in operation. Furthermore, they necessarily contain porosity that is used both to remove swarf and to supply coolant to the workpiece. If large enough, a pore can act as a defect that grows catastrophically in service, leading to fracture of the wheel. As wheel fracture is clearly undesirable, wheels are spun to 1.5 times their operating speed in a steel tank before they leave the factory. As the maximum stress in a grinding wheel is proportional to the square of its speed ($\sigma \propto v^2$), this proof test thus requires each wheel to survive 2.25 (i.e. 1.5^2) times its service stress before being allowed into service.

Proof testing has always been a godsend to engineers, as a proof-tested metal pressure vessel, for example, is in a better condition for service after testing – assuming that it survives! When a vessel is loaded well above its design load during proof stressing, stresses around notches and cracks exceed yield and so the material plastically deforms, usually without further cracking. This plastic deformation causes defects to be blunted, stress distributions to be evened out and, when the load is removed, residual compressive stresses to be left in what would otherwise be potentially dangerous areas.   △

In this part, I am going to consider primarily engineering metals, of which by far the most common are steels. The principles can be applied to other classes of material, but they find most application when designing with metals.

Ferrous metals of all kinds are very much cleaner than they were half a century ago; fewer impurities mean that they are much tougher and so less prone to dangerous, brittle fractures. The presence of notches, other stress raisers that are necessary in a particular design, and cracks introduced during fabrication is less of a problem than it was. However, there is plenty of safety-critical plant in operation that is half a century old, and failure assessments of such plant are routine to ensure that they continue to operate safely.

Historically, plant became heavier (because of the need for thicker sections to support operation at higher temperatures and pressures) at the same time as stronger, less-tough materials were being used. Concern over the behaviour of such structures in the presence of cracks – for example, vessels in the nuclear industry – stimulated research into fracture mechanics in order to consider, and so prevent, potential failure events. As ever, industrial development and regulatory procedures are triggered by accidents and the fear of accidents.

For example, in an aircraft structure made from forged and rolled metal that is riveted together, cracks are unlikely to be present when the plane is brand new; but they do grow by fatigue in service under repeated loading and unloading during flight and on the major loading excursions during landing and take off. If, as is likely, you have travelled in an aeroplane, you have certainly trusted your life to a cracked aluminium structure. Many cracks in an airframe are minor, but the economic life objective is for 19 out of 20 aeroplanes to exceed 20 years of operation without major fatigue cracking in the primary structure. This means that, in a structure that just meets this design objective, 1 out of 20 aeroplanes may crack prior to 20 years of service. These statistics predict that in a large fleet of aeroplanes the earliest fatigue cracking could occur as early as midway through the aeroplane's design life.

The prediction of fatigue crack growth based on fracture mechanics concepts is a very powerful tool for assessing crack growth in the airline industry. For example, the limit to stable growth of a fatigue crack occurs when the (long) crack grows in a fast, unstable fashion by tearing through the thin panels (Figure 1.1) and possibly by brittle failure through thicker spars. So, if you can calculate the growth rate of a crack you will be able to determine whether failure is imminent or not.

At the other end of the design spectrum are structures that are designed for infinite life, and so don't have such problems. For example, the designer of a monocoque car structure is far more concerned with crumple zones that dictate the plastic collapse of a car body in a crash. However, the designer of a car is not as concerned with the need to minimize weight as the aircraft designer: aeroplanes designed like cars would remain firmly land-bound.

Different industries use different metals in different sizes under different design constraints, and so they use our understanding of how cracks grow and how cracked structures might fail in different ways. The designer of the light, thin-walled, aluminium pressure vessel that is a civil aeroplane (military aircraft are not pressurized) has a completely different set of problems from the designer of the four-inch-thick, hot, steel pressure vessel that is a nuclear reactor. Although the understanding of cracked metal under load is built on the same theoretical and

Figure 1.1   Part of the body of the Aloha Airlines Boeing 737, which lost a section of the fuselage owing to fatigue cracking

practical foundations in both cases, the resulting engineering practice is completely different. As a result, experience shows there is little or no movement of specialized engineers between, say, Rolls Royce Marine and British Aerospace.

The theories that we have to describe the dynamic behaviour of a crack growing under an increasing load are, quite frankly, not very good. However, the notion that engineering is built on the ability to predict a type of behaviour as exactly as possible is naive. Engineering practice is a combination of theories, analysis, experiment and codes that produces conservative, and therefore reliable, results. Safety factors collect together the variabilities in materials and the uncertainties in the design and assessment processes (again, these are industry specific) to produce reserve factors on load that are acceptable.

A key factor in all the industries that have to live with cracks is the inspection processes. Cracks that break the surface can be found by observant aircraft cleaners or by painting with special paints, and cracks buried in the body of a part might be found using non-destructive techniques (NDT) based on X-rays or ultrasonics. Again, the inspection methods vary with different industries and the characteristics of their products, but inspection procedures are integral to the design and operation of safety-critical structures and plant in all industries.

1.2 Materials properties and testing

You know from Block 1 that engineering materials under load are routinely characterized using a tensile test to measure yield stress (or 0.2% proof stress) and tensile strength: a structure designed to carry two-thirds of its yield stress is regarded as highly stressed.

Stress is the engineering measure that takes the geometry out of a problem; doubling the cross section of a bar at the same time as doubling the axial load leaves the stress on the section the same. Stress has the property of *similitude*: if I know the stress in a small laboratory specimen will be the same as that in a large component or structure, I can perform an assessment of the one based on the results from the other. So stress is the *lingua franca* that allows us to relate the result of my laboratory test to your huge, expensive structure on which many lives and jobs depend.

At the beginning of the twentieth century it was found that tensile test results were not sufficient to characterize the failure of notched parts, particularly when the notch is sharp – as it is with screw threads, for example. Similitude did not work, which was a huge shock, as it was expected that increasing the cross section would reduce the stress and so improve the design of the part. In fact, in the presence of a sharp notch this simply isn't the case.

DVD

The Charpy test can be seen as part of the 'Liberty ships' programme on the DVD; tensile testing is shown in the 'Testing of materials and structures' programme.

A new type of test was needed. The test that was developed to characterize the toughness of a material, as opposed to its tensile strength, was the Charpy test – a test that is still used today. In a Charpy test, a high load is applied to a sample using a swinging hammer that strikes a notched bar (this is not a shock load, as the hammer swings relatively slowly). The toughness of the bar is measured by the energy lost from the hammer in fracturing the bar. Brittle fractures absorb less energy than ductile fractures.

The pendulum machines used in a Charpy test are cheap, simple and quick to use for making measurements at a range of temperatures. Such tests are carried out according to the procedures of international standards that capture both custom and practice in order to ensure that their results are compatible across test-houses in different countries. The resulting Charpy V-notch energy (CVN or C_v) is a measure of toughness. However, it cannot be used to predict the failure of a large structure from the performance of small specimens; the CVN value measured in the Charpy test does not have the property of similitude, and cannot be used to predict failure in a larger structure. But it does provide a good, qualitative idea of whether a failure might be brittle or ductile, and it is hugely practical:

> It can readily be seen that in the use of these very small test pieces lies one of the chief merits of the whole system, it being possible to cut specimens from crop ends of shafts, odd scraps from machinery and very often from the finished product without injuring its strength or appearance, further the cost of preparation of the specimen is very small, and storing and recording of the fractured sample for future reference is greatly simplified.

> E. G. Izod talking about his own version of the Charpy test.

Engineers in the early 1900s were attempting to identify 'brittle steel'. Nowadays, the idea that a *material* is brittle can be grossly misleading. Rather, we would have you classify *fractures* as brittle. An example of our favoured, pedantic statement is 'glass is a material that normally fractures in a brittle fashion', rather than the more conversationally normal 'glass is a brittle material'.

Some steels will fail in a dangerous manner by brittle fracture at a particular size (say that of a pressure vessel), but fail in a safer fashion by energy-absorbing ductile mechanisms at a smaller size (say that of a test specimen). Together with the need for materials characterizing numbers, this led to the development of the modern fracture toughness test that is currently embodied in BS EN ISO 12737:2005. The fracture toughness test involves growing a fatigue crack in a specimen, then carefully loading it to failure while monitoring the applied load and the opening of the crack.

Therefore, the fracture toughness test is expensive, and so it has not superseded the Charpy test; buying a value of fracture toughness to British Standards costs about £300 per number at the time of writing, whereas a Charpy test is about a tenth of the price, with a 10% discount for the usual set of three. But the more costly test does give similitude: the fracture toughness value at which the small sample fails will be the same as that at which the large pressure vessel fails, if it fails by brittle fracture.

I turn now to the use of engineering theory. Numerical analysis has transformed engineering. Almost all modern engineering practice in structural and failure analysis is built on the use of computers to perform numerical analyses using finite element (FE) software – this is the only way that our theories can be applied to complex geometries. An FE analysis that is specific to your problem is expensive, and so the results numerical analyses of important (common) problems are captured on data sheets or encapsulated in other software. Here I shall combine numerical analysis with theoretical models and the results of testing in exactly the same way that they are combined in current industrial practice.

The practical fracture mechanics techniques that you will learn in this block are those that are in current use: people earn their living in this way.

1.3 The story so far

There are several key messages that I want you to take away from reading this introduction:

- Proof testing to loads above the design load benefits metal structures.

- Cracks in operating structures are common.

- Structures containing cracks are routinely inspected and assessed.

- Tensile tests scale (i.e. show similitude), but some toughness tests do not.

- There are traditional and modern standards for measuring toughness.

2 LINEAR-ELASTIC FRACTURE MECHANICS

2.1 Brittle and ductile fracture

A perfectly brittle failure leaves no visual trace of plasticity on the broken surfaces of the specimen. So, the two broken halves of a part that has failed in such a manner can be fitted back together perfectly, showing only a line of separation on the surface – remember the broken mug you saw in Block 1 Part 3. Brittle fractures propagate extremely quickly, moving at between about 40% and 100% of the speed of sound in the material. Figure 1.2 shows a brittle, flat fracture in a small, steel specimen that initiated from a fatigue crack grown from a machined notch.

The fragment in Figure 1.2 is half of a specimen that fractured when loaded in bending. The load–deflection trace (Figure 1.3) was linear until the bang of a fast fracture was heard. If the specimen had been unloaded before fast, brittle fracture broke it into two pieces, then the trace would have gone straight back to the origin. A fracture of this type is known as *linear-elastic*: linear because the path is a straight line and elastic because the load trace goes up and down the same path.

By way of a complete contrast, look at the fracture surface in Figure 1.4. A specimen made from a different steel, of a similar size to that shown in Figure 1.2, has failed from a fatigue crack in a way that shows evidence of considerable plastic deformation during failure: the heavily distorted fracture surface means that the two halves of the test-piece cannot be fitted back together. The massive plasticity associated with such a failure generates a non-linear load–deflection curve, as shown in Figure 1.5.

Figure 1.2 and Figure 1.4 show different steels that fail in different ways when tested under the same conditions with samples of about the same size. However (and this is one of the major issues in fracture mechanics), a specimen that fails in a ductile manner in a small section can fail in a fast, brittle fashion in larger sections. The implication of this is profound: in the presence of a crack, increasing

DVD

Toughness testing using samples such as those shown in Figures 1.2 and 1.4 is covered in the 'Toughness testing: Corus case study' programme on the DVD. You have not yet been introduced to all the concepts in that programme, but you may want to watch it now and revisit it later.

Figure 1.2   A flat, brittle fracture

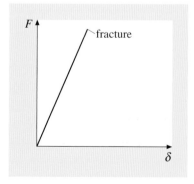

Figure 1.3   Linear load–deflection trace from a toughness test

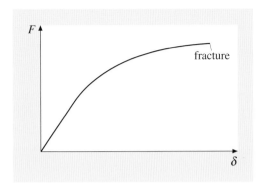

Figure 1.5   Non-linear load–deflection trace

Figure 1.4   A distorted,
ductile fracture

the size of the part does not necessarily improve its performance because the same
metal can fail in different ways depending on the size of the section containing an
initiating flaw.

2.2 The linear-elastic fracture mechanics equation

The most dangerous form of failure in a cracked structure is brittle fracture. As we
have seen, where a crack interacts with the right conditions of specimen geometry
and loading, metals that show significant ductility in a simple tensile test will fail in a
brittle manner, with no apparent plastic behaviour at all.

Fortunately, although our theories for cracks growing dynamically under a gradually
increasing load are not all that good, the theory that predicts the onset of fast, brittle
fracture is quite remarkable in its accuracy. The linear-elastic fracture mechanics
(LEFM) theory is a unique mechanics solution for an infinitely sharp crack in a body
under load where the material's response to applied loading is linear.

There is no assumption or incorporation of plasticity in LEFM theory. However, in
a cracked metal body under load there is always some plasticity at a crack tip. If a
crack tip were infinitely sharp, then the stress ahead of the crack would shoot off
to infinity; in practice, plasticity intervenes to blunt the crack (Figure 1.6). There is
a very small amount of yielding at the crack tip (called *small-scale yielding*), but
it doesn't matter what happens in this region because it is the surrounding elastic
field that controls the fracture event; hence the stress in the fracture mechanics
equation is the far-field stress. This is the argument that allows us to use LEFM
theory for metals, and effectively to ignore the small plastic region around the tip
of the crack.

One reason that LEFM theory is remarkably useful is that there is a *pattern* of
stresses ahead of a crack tip (Figure 1.7) that is always of the same form for the same
mode of loading; only the magnitude of this pattern depends on the loading and the
geometry of the component.

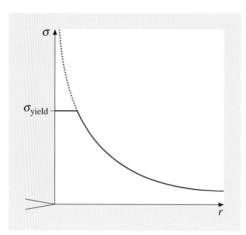

Figure 1.6   The magnitude of the stress field at a distance r from the crack tip would tend towards infinity as r goes to zero, but there is always some plasticity that limits its maximum value

Note that the stress intensity factor has no relation to the stress concentration factors you encountered in Block 1, which are a result of changes in geometry.

The magnitude of the stress field is embodied by a single parameter, the *stress intensity factor* K_I. It's a good name because K_I sums up the stress state at the crack tip in just one number, its intensity. If two cracks have the same intensity number, then the material ahead of the crack tip is in exactly the same loaded state. How useful is that?!

So, how do we determine K_I? The simplest of all geometries for studying crack problems is a conceptual one. Figure 1.8 shows a centre crack in an infinite plate in tension, for which case there are only two parameters that K_I can depend on: the far-field stress σ, which characterizes the load, and the length of crack, defined as $2a$ by convention for an embedded crack; this crack length is the only measure of geometry for an infinite plate.

We find that the stress intensity factor K_I is related to stress and the square root of the crack length and we write $K_I \propto \sigma\sqrt{\pi a}$, and deduce that its units are the unusual MN m$^{-3/2}$, or MPa √m. The π, though inconvenient, is there for historical reasons.

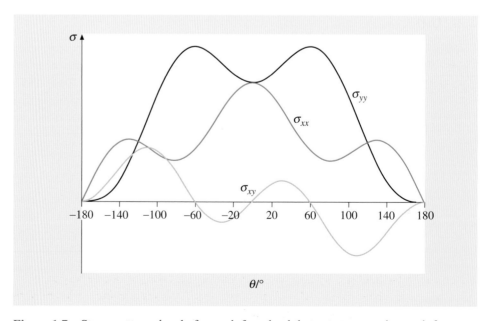

Figure 1.7   Stress pattern ahead of a crack for a load that acts to open the crack faces

To take account of different geometries, say an edge crack rather than a centre crack (Figure 1.9), we put in a dimensionless number to produce the LEFM equation:

$$K_I = Y\sigma\sqrt{\pi a} \tag{1.1}$$

where $Y = 1$ for an embedded crack in the notionally infinite plate shown in Figure 1.8. For an edge crack in an infinite plate (Figure 1.9), where by convention the length of crack is defined as a, $Y = 1.12$. Values of Y are found in handbooks – more on this later.

You may have come across the LEFM equation previously. If you haven't, fear not, as with only four variables it is easy to understand. However, you will need to know the definitions of the variables in this equation to be able to apply it in practice.

To summarize:

- The LEFM equation is the key equation for studying fracture. It describes fast, brittle fracture where there is no gross evidence of plastic deformation on the fracture surface.

- K_I is the crack-tip characterizing parameter, called the stress intensity factor. It is a measure of the magnitude of the stress field near a crack tip. The stress intensity factor applies to sharp cracks. Like stress, the stress intensity factor can be used to compare different problems: any crack in a body that has the same K_I as another crack in another body is effectively in the same condition.

- Y is a dimensionless parameter that accounts for the geometry in which the crack is contained.

- σ is the stress in the body of the material away from the crack (the so-called far-field stress).

- a is the length of an edge crack or one-half the length of an embedded crack.

Figure 1.8   Centre crack in an infinite plate

Figure 1.9   Edge crack in an infinite plate

EXAMPLE

A bar contains a 4 mm edge crack, and is loaded with a far-field tensile stress of 100 MPa. If the value of Y is 1.2 for the geometry concerned, what is the value of the stress intensity at the crack tip?

SOLUTION

Using Equation (1.1) the stress intensity is:

$$K_I = Y\sigma\sqrt{\pi a}$$
$$= 1.2 \times 100 \text{ MPa} \times \sqrt{\pi \times 4 \times 10^{-3}} \text{ m}$$
$$= 13.5 \text{ MPa } \sqrt{\text{m}}$$

Note that the far-field stresses in Figure 1.8 and Figure 1.9 act in such a way as to open the crack. The subscript 'I' in K_I indicates that the crack is being loaded by such stresses normal to the direction of the crack opening.

Figure 1.10   Cracking in shear from a central saw cut in a Perspex plate

Clearly, it is possible to have remote stresses that act in a different direction, relative to the crack, from those shown in Figures 1.8 and 1.9.

Figure 1.10 shows a Perspex® panel loaded in pure shear, as indicated by the arrows around the edges. So, in the plane of the crack the crack-tip stress pattern will be caused by shear stresses, but note that the crack did not grow in the direction of its original plane. Instead, the two cracks grew from the central saw cut in the direction dictated by the maximum opening load stresses, not in the directions dictated by the remote (shear) stresses.

EXERCISE 1.1

Draw the directions of the principal tensile stresses that open the crack on Figure 1.10.

However, in fibrous materials with weak interfaces in the direction of the central saw cut, a crack might grow in the direction of the shear loading and in this case the subscript II is used, i.e. K_{II}, to distinguish that the crack is progressing under the influence of a different mode of loading; but in common, homogeneous materials cracks grow in the direction dictated by the maximum opening stresses. In this part, I am going to deal only with cracks being opened by stresses normal to the direction of the crack. If the subscript is not present in a paper or book, then you can assume that K refers to the opening K_I; you can also make the same assumption in this course. The different possible modes of loading a crack are shown in Figure 1.11; by far the most prevalent in practice is mode I.

With the single parameter K_I you can characterize the crack driving force in any loaded component. So, if K_I in my specimen is the same as K_I in your complex and expensive plant, then, as long as there is not much plasticity present (i.e. LEFM is a valid theory to use), my crack-tip conditions are the same as yours; and when my (cheap) specimen goes bang I can use the result to predict when your expensive plant will fail and charge you a fee for the service. So, unlike the Charpy measure of toughness, an LEFM measure of toughness can be used to predict failure.

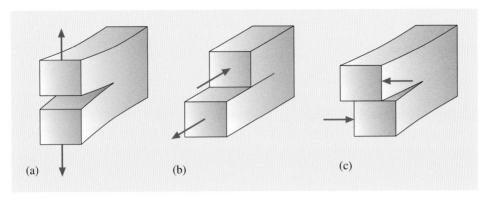

Figure 1.11   The three modes of loading a crack: (a) tensile opening (mode I); (b) in-plane sliding or shear (mode II); (c) anti-plane shear (mode III)

Another way of considering K is as a crack-driving parameter: for a given geometry, you can keep increasing the load and so increase K_I at the crack tip. This is analogous to increasing the load and so increasing the stress in a section. However, just as is the case with stress, there comes a point at which the material can no longer resist the stress intensity. In the case of stress, the stress that causes plastic deformation to occur is known as a yield stress (or in practice define a 0.2% proof stress). The yield stress is a material property. In fracture mechanics, the material property is known as the *fracture toughness* of the material – K_{IC} for the case of K_I. This material property is a limiting value on the mechanics driving force of stress intensity.

So, the essence of LEFM is contained in the equation:

$$K_I = Y\sigma\sqrt{\pi a} = K_{IC} \text{ at failure} \qquad (1.2)$$

The values of the variables in the fracture mechanics equation are often uncertain. For example, materials properties and/or crack lengths might be unknown ('no records, Guv, it was built in 1950, you know') and so values will need to be assumed. How such problems are dealt with depends on industrial practice, experience, and agreed standards.

LEFM is a theory of brittle fracture: the lowest energy fracture that can occur in a metal. With common, modern steels in ordinary-sized sections, such fractures occur rarely, and yet LEFM is a useful theory simply because it can produce conservative results. If a simple stress analysis produces a result that is either correct or lower than that which would be achieved by a more complex (and, therefore, more expensive) analysis, then the simple analysis will be used if its results are acceptable: there is no point being more accurate than is required to solve a problem. Such analyses are called lower-bound solutions; any decision based on such an analysis will be a conservative decision.

This goes against the simple view that the aim of engineering analysis is to predict what *will* happen, if you are designing, or what *did* happen, if you are troubleshooting or doing lucrative forensic engineering.

The difficulties in applying the LEFM equation lie in deciding whether it is appropriate to a problem and what are sensible values to use in a specific, practical context.

2.3 The parameters of linear-elastic fracture mechanics

In this section I shall consider each of the variables in the fracture mechanics equation in turn, with a view to assigning some values to them and practising calculation with the fracture mechanics equation.

2.3.1 Fracture toughness K_{IC}

K_{IC} is the material property that predicts fast, brittle fracture when $K_I = K_{IC}$. K_{IC} is measured from a test conducted to a standard such as BS EN ISO 12737, or ASTM E399. Table 1.1 gives some indicative values of K_{IC}.

Table 1.1 K_{IC} values for a range of materials

Material	K_{IC}/MPa $\sqrt{m}$
Modern, high-strength steels	50–200
Older, lower-quality steels	down to 40
Titanium alloys	50–100
Aluminium alloys	20–40
Cast irons	6–20
Glass	0.5

Clearly, the range of K_{IC} values for different metal alloys is wide, which is because toughness depends critically on the type of alloy and the state of its heat treatment. Notice that an aluminium alloy can have a toughness value the same as that of a cast iron, which, perhaps, illustrates the danger of referring to materials as being brittle. Aluminium alloys are not very tough, in absolute terms, but they are usually used in thin sections, so brittle failure tends to be unusual. However, Figure 1.12 shows an aircraft spar that has failed in service with very little plastic deformation visible on the fracture surface.

Figure 1.12   Failed aircraft spar

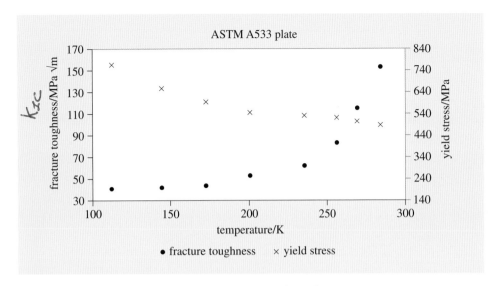

Figure 1.13   Relationship between yield stress and toughness

For a particular alloy that can be heat treated to produce different strengths, we usually find that high strength is 'bought' at the expense of toughness and that for a particular alloy at different temperatures the strength and toughness are inversely related. Figure 1.13 shows the relationship between yield stress (strength) and toughness for a high-quality steel plate. This remarkable dataset shows that the yield stress of this steel increases by 58% while the fracture toughness falls by 73% as the temperature falls: an example of the ☑ **ductile-to-brittle transition temperature** ☑. High strength and high toughness are difficult to achieve at the same time.

☑ Ductile-to-brittle transition temperature

In general, the toughness of materials tends to fall as the temperature is reduced. The energy-absorbing mechanisms in materials that lead to good toughness tend to work better when there is some thermal energy to help activate them.

Many steels exhibit an extreme example of this, with a sharp transition from ductile failures to brittle failures over a relatively narrow range of temperature.

This is most pronounced in ferritic steels, where the crystal structure is body-centred cubic. If that means nothing to you, don't worry. Austenitic steels, which have a face-centred cubic structure, do not show a pronounced transition. This is an example of how the structure of a material on the atomic scale can have an influence on its macroscopic mechanical behaviour.

For an example of how the ductile-to-brittle transition can have a significant influence on the performance of steels in practice, watch the 'Liberty ships' programme on the course DVD.   ◺

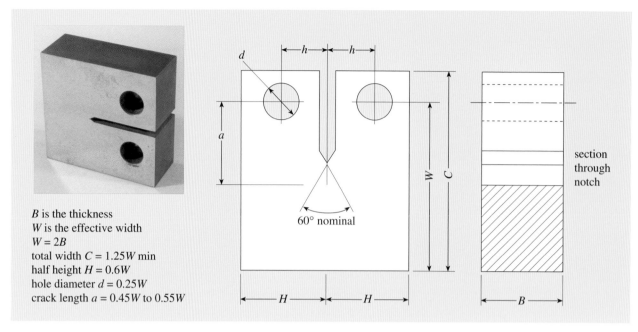

B is the thickness
W is the effective width
$W = 2B$
total width $C = 1.25W$ min
half height $H = 0.6W$
hole diameter $d = 0.25W$
crack length $a = 0.45W$ to $0.55W$

Figure 1.14   A CT specimen showing the recommended ratios from BS EN ISO 12737

Material properties such as K_{IC} need to be measured, and engineers depend on standards to specify how they are measured, so that data from different sources can be compared and used reliably. Standards reflect the traditions in different industrial sectors. To measure K_{IC}, the geometry of the test-piece being loaded is important: the aircraft industry likes the compact tension (CT) specimen shown in Figure 1.14, whereas bend specimens (Figure 1.15) are favoured by the pipeline and pressure-vessel industries. There are various historical factors lying behind such traditions; the standards are written to allow for both approaches, and for the results obtained from the different approaches to be comparable. The geometry and loading of a bend specimen serve to magnify the load on the cracked ligament, which is a benefit to industries that use tough materials; in contrast, the CT geometry is useful because it is economical with material.

Both test specimens have a notch from which a fatigue crack is grown into the body of the material; the intention is to grow the crack to a sufficient length that it is away from any effects of the tip of the notch and the loading pins.

A valid fracture toughness test needs to produce a flat, low-energy, brittle fracture. If a range of specimens with varying thickness *B* is tested, it is found that the load [stress intensity factor] needed to cause fracture gets progressively lower as the test-piece gets bigger. The failure load is asymptotic to a minimum value, as shown in Figure 1.16; it is this minimum value that is the materials property K_{IC}. The purpose of a standard document is to recommend a set of procedures that will produce a 'true', valid value of K_{IC} economically, i.e. without using overlarge test-pieces. Figure 1.16 also shows what are called 'shear lips' on the edges, i.e. free surfaces, of the advancing crack front. These shear lips are produced by the unconstrained plasticity at the free surface.

Look back to the small specimen shown in Figure 1.2, where there are no shear lips. If the metal being tested is not very ductile, then the plasticity ahead of the fatigue

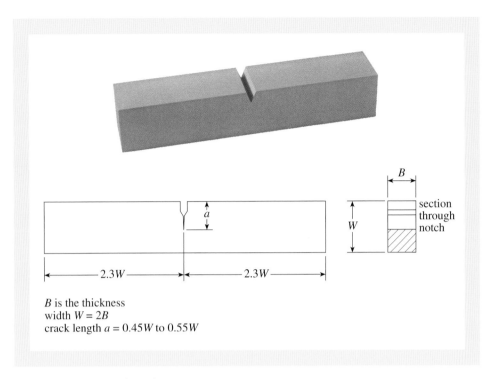

Figure 1.15   A bend specimen

crack tip is small and relatively easily contained by a small body of elastic material; hence, a small test specimen is fine. If the metal is ductile, then the larger plastic zone needs more elastic material to contain it; hence, a large test specimen is needed.

The stress state along a crack front is complex. In the centre of the crack the material ahead of the tip is in plane strain; at the free surface the material is in plane stress. It is this change in stress state that creates a larger plastic zone along the crack front, which is shown in Figure 1.17.

DVD

For an illustration of the variation of the stress state along the crack front, watch the 'Plane strain animation' programme on the DVD.

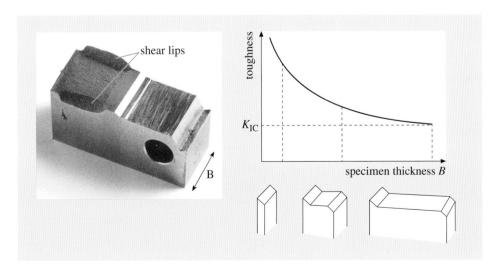

Figure 1.16   The effect of specimen thickness on the toughness

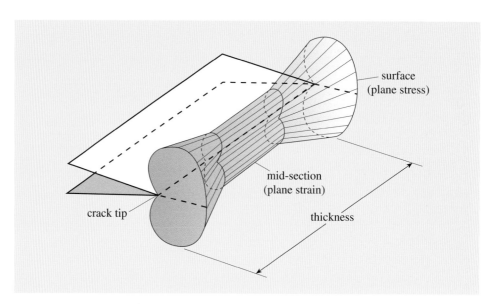

Figure 1.17   The shape of the plastically deformed material and how it varies at the crack tip (usually referred to as the crack-tip plastic zone)

When the shear lips are small compared with the total surface of flat fracture, this is a sign that most of the material is in plane strain, and the test is likely to produce a valid LEFM fracture toughness.

The rule of thumb adopted by standards is that the key dimensions of cracked specimens need to be about 50 times greater than the size of the crack-tip plastic zone in order to produce valid LEFM conditions. British Standard BS EN ISO 12737 gives these size criteria for LEFM specimens as:

$$B, a \geq 2.5 \left(\frac{K_Q}{\sigma_{\text{yield}}} \right)^2 \tag{1.3}$$

i.e. both the specimen's final crack length before it is fractured and its thickness B need to exceed this value, calculated from K_Q (the provisional value of K_{IC} when the test is complete). In practice, an estimate of K_{IC} will be made beforehand in selecting an appropriate specimen size.

SAQ 1.1 (Learning outcome 1.1)

(a) An aluminium alloy has an estimated toughness K_{IC} of 32 MPa √m and a yield stress of 380 MPa. What value of B will be needed to obtain a valid measure of K_{IC}, according to British Standard BS EN ISO 12737?

(b) Use Equation (1.3) to calculate what the Standards recommend for the thickness B at the extremes of temperature for the steel shown in Figure 1.13.

The answer to SAQ 1.1 shows that a remarkably wide range of sizes can be necessary for fracture toughness tests, which are genuinely seen in practice. The photograph

Figure 1.18   Little and large; the small specimen is about 20 mm in width

in Figure 1.18 was taken in the laboratories at Corus. The bottom specimen is half of a broken CT sample of a nuclear pressure-vessel steel; on top is a whole CT sample made from a high-strength, low-ductility steel.

If you have, or can buy, a valid fracture toughness for your material, in the relevant condition and at the temperature of interest (this might not be the design temperature, but, say, some thermal shock temperature that is lower than the operating temperature), then you are well on the way to applying LEFM.

Often valid LEFM-based toughness data are not available. Safety cases are needed for plant routinely designed and built from materials without K_{IC} data; indeed, much existing plant has little or no original documentation. By far the most common toughness data available, achievable or affordable is a measure of C_v.

The Charpy test is a cheap and cheerful swinging-hammer test, compared with the more complex and instrumented K_{IC} test. There is, of course, some commonality in the values obtained from the two tests for the same material, as both measure fracture resistance, albeit in different ways: see ☑ **Charpy test correlations** ☑.

DVD

The practice of a Charpy test is shown in the 'Liberty ships' programme on the DVD.

☑ Charpy test correlations

Charpy energy measurements of toughness cannot be used predictively, unlike K_{IC} values. Because the Charpy test values are specific to the size of sample measured, they cannot necessarily be extrapolated: there is no similitude. However, they are ubiquitous and cheap, so there is a continuing, strong interest in relating the results of a Charpy test to a K_{IC} value. So, what are the problems?

Figure 1.19 shows the results of Charpy tests on a ferritic steel at a range of different temperatures.   ▷

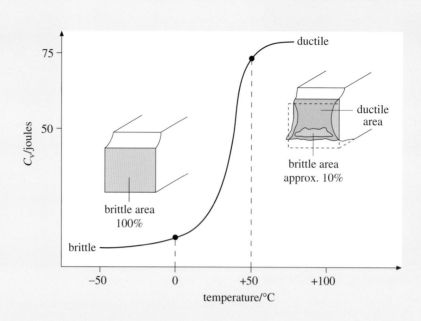

Figure 1.19   Charpy test results

For this material, at this size and at low temperatures, the fracture process does not consume much energy, the fracture surface sparkles and the two halves fit back together: the fracture is by brittle cleavage on this 'lower shelf' of the diagram.

On the 'upper shelf' there is a small sparkling area surrounded by dull, deformed fracture surface (dimpled rupture) that has consumed much more energy during its creation: the fracture is ductile, the two halves do not fit back together and gross plastic deformation is seen close to the free surfaces.

The temperature halfway between the upper and lower shelves is called the transition temperature or the ductile-to-brittle transition temperature.

Not all engineering metals show such a sharply defined change in fracture with temperature. There is a striking difference between the fracture behaviour of austenitic and ferritic steels, for instance.

Typically, a Charpy specimen is about 10 mm wide, and, as K_{IC} is sensitive to size, relating Charpy results to fracture toughness values is very difficult. However, it is also critical whether, at the operating temperature, an engineering part will cleave or tear. If an engineering structure is bigger than 10 mm, then Charpy test results will not necessarily translate from specimen to structure. Charpy energy values cannot be used to predict the performance of an engineering part; they are a property of the test.

All these arguments militate against the likelihood of a useful general relationship between Charpy toughnesses and K_{IC}; but the need cannot be ignored! So, there are many published correlations in the literature that are specific to particular materials and that try to distinguish between fractures on the upper and lower shelves, and through the transition regime when these materials are ferritic. British Standards give advice on using a master curve based on Charpy results; however, guidance in standards is conservative, hedged around with conditions and not applicable to older steels.

Modern pressure-vessel steels with C_v values no greater than 70 J and no less than 7 J were studied in 1973 to produce the expression $K_{IC} = 14.7C_v^{0.5}$, with a scatter band of $\pm 15\%$. A recent Structural Integrity Assessment Procedure for European Industry (SINTAP) document suggests a lower bound relationship for steel of $K_{IC} = 12C_v^{0.5}$, which is a little lower than the bottom of the scatter band of the 1973 study. The SINTAP recommendation is the only relationship that we shall use here.

EXERCISE 1.2

(a) What range of fracture toughnesses is obtained between C_v values of 7 to 70 J:

    (i)   using the 1973 expression $K_{IC} = 14.7C_v^{0.5}$

    (ii) using the SINTAP expression?

(b) What proportion of the range of fracture toughnesses for steels does this cover?

(c) What would be the expected Charpy toughness, using the SINTAP relationship, for an aluminium alloy with a toughness of 30 MPa $\sqrt{m}$?

Key concepts

The key concepts to take away from this section are:

- Values of K_{IC} for engineering metals cover a wide range. A 'tough' material might have a K_{IC} of 30 MPa $\sqrt{m}$, though many steels have values in excess of 100 MPa $\sqrt{m}$.

- Alloying metals and heat treating them can produce high strength, but at the expense of toughness.

- Fracture toughness tends to fall with reducing temperature.

- The stress state along a crack front in a fracture toughness specimen changes from plane strain in the centre to plane stress at the edges.

- Plane stress failure produces shear lips at the edges of the specimen.

- CT and bending specimens are specified in international standards for the measurement of K_{IC}, and a valid fracture toughness measurement requires most of the fracture surface to be under plane strain conditions.

2.3.2 Geometrical factor Y

The dimensionless factor Y in the fracture mechanics equation accounts for the geometry in which the crack is present and the size of the unique stress pattern within that geometry.

EXERCISE 1.3

(a) What is the value of Y for a centre crack in an infinite plate under tension, and how is the length of the centre crack expressed?

(b) What is the value of Y for an edge crack in an infinite plate under tension, and how is the length of the edge crack expressed?

If a plate is of finite size (as, of course, is always the case in reality), then the crack tip is affected by the free boundary and K_I is larger than is the case when the boundary is far distant. This is because the stress field in the presence of the crack depends on the geometry in which it exists. Y accounts for this geometry effect: the closer the tip is to the boundary, the higher the value of Y and so the higher the value of K_I.

Equations that describe the change in Y are obtained from curve fitting of FE solutions; they are available in handbooks, just like the stress concentration factors you saw in Block 1. The convention in these handbooks is usually that an embedded crack is $2a$ long and an edge crack is a long (Figures 1.8 and 1.20 are examples of embedded cracks, whereas Figures 1.9 and 1.21 show edge cracks). Embedded cracks have two tips, so 'two tips $2a$' is a useful aide-memoire. The same convention has come to be used on the width of the plate: $2W$ where the crack is embedded, W when it is an edge crack.

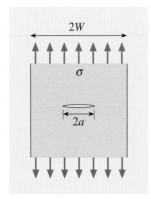

Figure 1.20 Embedded crack in a plate of finite width

All the Y relationships that you will need in this block are in the calculators on your DVD, which you will use in a while. You will never have to remember a specific value for Y for a particular geometry, though it's helpful if you remember that $Y = 1$ occurs only in the case of an embedded crack in an infinite plate. In this part, I shall just consider these two geometries of an embedded crack and an edge crack where the boundaries affect the value of Y.

For illustration, the equation for a through-thickness centre crack in a plate of finite width in tension, Figure 1.20, is:

$$K_I = Y\sigma\sqrt{\pi a} = \left[\frac{1 - 0.025\left(\dfrac{a}{W}\right)^2 + 0.06\left(\dfrac{a}{W}\right)^4}{\sqrt{\cos\left(\dfrac{\pi a}{2W}\right)}} \right] \sigma\sqrt{\pi a}$$

Note that, in this equation, as the plate widens and so a/W becomes smaller, then Y approaches unity, i.e. the value for an infinite plate.

An edge crack in a finite-width plate (Figure 1.21) is not, as one might think by considering symmetry, the equivalent of half an embedded crack, because the slope at the centre of the gaping crack in an infinite plate is constrained, whereas it is free at the mouth of an edge crack. (Imagine an embedded crack: at its centre the slope of the two surfaces is constrained to be horizontal before curving down to the opposite tip. If you imagine an edge crack as half of an embedded crack, then there is nothing on the other side to constrain the slope of the two surfaces.) This freedom to gape can be thought of as effectively 'moving' the load to the crack tip, and thus increasing K.

Figure 1.21 Edge crack in a plate of finite width

For an edge crack in an infinite plate (Figure 1.9) under tension $Y = 1.12$, so:

$$K_I = Y\sigma\sqrt{\pi a} = 1.12\,\sigma\sqrt{\pi a}$$

The equation that takes into account the width of a finite edge-cracked plate is:

$$K_I = \left[1.12 - 0.23\frac{a}{W} + 10.55\left(\frac{a}{W}\right)^2 - 21.72\left(\frac{a}{W}\right)^3 + 30.39\left(\frac{a}{W}\right)^4\right]\sigma\sqrt{\pi a}$$

Comfortingly, in this equation Y approaches 1.12 as the plate becomes wider and a/W becomes smaller.

Note that in both of these geometries the crack is infinitely long out of the plane of the paper.

EXERCISE 1.4

Figure 1.22 shows the Y calibration curve for a plate in tension with a through-thickness edge crack.

(a) By reading directly from the curve, estimate Y when the crack is one-quarter of the way through the thickness W of the plate.

(b) Estimate the percentage change in Y as the crack grows to (i) one-half and (ii) three-quarters through the thickness.

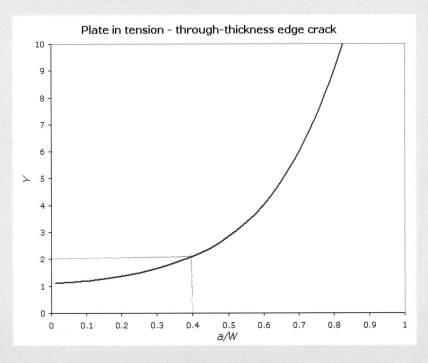

Figure 1.22 Y calibration for an edge-cracked plate loaded in tension

The answer to Exercise 1.4 shows that, as a crack grows, the value of Y can increase dramatically. So, either knowing or making an assumption about the nearness of a crack front to a boundary is critical to the practice of fracture mechanics.

DVD

The 'K calculator' is in the computer-based activities section of the DVD.

Figure 1.22 comes from the 'K calculator'. Open the spreadsheet now. The first sheet is called 'Brittle fracture'. You can choose different calibration factors from the drop-down menu. Select the option for a plate in tension with a through-thickness edge crack and then look at the second sheet titled 'Y calibration'. The graph of Y against a/W should look like the one in Figure 1.22.

SAQ 1.2 (Learning outcomes 1.2–1.4)

Have a look at how Y changes with a/W for an edge-cracked beam or plate in pure bending, rather than in tension, using the K calculator and repeat Exercise 1.4.

Notice from the answer to SAQ 1.2 that K_I does not increase with crack length anywhere near as rapidly under bending as under tension. This is because the stress distribution in bending varies from tension to compression across the section, so there are compressive stresses ahead of the crack.

I now want to consider a plate or beam with an edge crack that finds itself in a combination of a tensile stress field and a bending stress field.

EXERCISE 1.5 (BLOCK 1 REVISION)

Sketch the distributions of stresses in a beam or plate under a combination of a tensile and a bending load.

I am most interested in a crack that finds itself subjected to the maximum tensile stresses; Exercise 1.5 showed that this occurs where the stresses of $\sigma_{tension}$ and $\sigma_{bending}$ combine to open the crack.

I have two very different Y calibration curves for tension and bending, and clearly I cannot simply choose one of them, arbitrarily, and use it for $\sigma_{tension} + \sigma_{bending}$. No, in stress fields of different forms the general rule is that the K values are added, not the stresses that cause them. So, I need to use the two Y calibration curves for the different stress distributions and add the resulting K values to produce a crack-driving parameter for the case of combined tension and bending.

(Note that Y calibration curves can be found using either the applied stress or the applied load. In the K calculator for an edge-cracked plate under tension and in bending I have used stress.)

EXERCISE 1.6

Calculate, longhand, the combined K for a through-thickness crack that has grown one-quarter of the distance from the tensile surface (i.e. a/W = 0.25) in a piece of 10 mm × 30 mm bar (Figure 1.23) under a tensile stress of 100 MPa and a bending stress that varies from +100 MPa to −100 MPa.

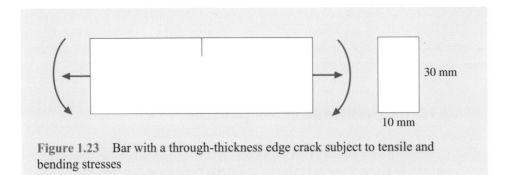

Figure 1.23   Bar with a through-thickness edge crack subject to tensile and bending stresses

Let's now consider further the far-field stress by which a crack is opened.

2.3.3 Far-field stress σ

The stress in the fracture mechanics equation:

$$K_I = Y\sigma\sqrt{\pi a}$$

is the far-field stress distribution in which the crack finds itself (computed from simple mechanics equations, handbooks or specific, expensive numerical calculations). K_I deals with the complex stress field at the crack tip – there is no application of a stress concentration factor. It is a common mistake to throw in a few stress concentrations for luck.

In this block I shall be quite cavalier about using the nearest available stress distribution to that of a particular problem with which I am concerned – so long as it is of a similar form.

For example, let's consider an edge crack in the wall of a pipe that is under pressure (Figure 1.24). Modelling the stress distribution in the pipe wall as a membrane stress, the crack can be considered as acting in a tensile stress field calculated using:

$$\sigma = p\frac{r}{t} \tag{1.4}$$

where p is the internal pressure, r the mean radius of the pipe and t is the wall thickness (as long as the mean pipe radius is much larger than the wall thickness).

The calculated value of stress can then be entered directly into the fracture mechanics equation using the Y calibration for an edge-cracked, finite-width plate. Note that

In the terminology of pipes, a 'membrane' stress is one that is uniform through the pipe wall: for example, a stress caused by the internal pressure in a thin-walled pipe. This distinguishes such a stress from a bending stress in the pipe wall that varies through the wall thickness.

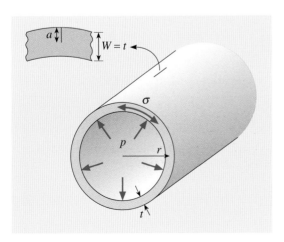

Figure 1.24   Stress in a pipe wall

this calibration does not take into account the curvature of the pipe wall; there are such calibrations but I don't have one to hand, so we will use what we have and assume that, as long as the radius is large compared with the wall thickness, the error involved will be small. So, let's do it, longhand again.

SAQ 1.3 (Learning outcomes 1.4–1.6)

(a) A thin-walled pipe carries a pressure of 15 MPa. It has a mean radius of 120 mm and a wall thickness of 10 mm. Ignoring curvature effects on the stress distribution and the value of Y, calculate K_I for an internal edge crack that is a quarter of the way through the pipe wall.

(b) If the pipe was made from steel, would you expect this crack to cause a brittle failure at this pressure?

Remember: Y calibration curves for different geometries are different for different stress distributions and so stresses that require different calibration curves cannot be added – only the resulting K_I values can be added. The crack in a combination of a tensile stress field and a bending stress distribution that we considered earlier produced two values of K that were added to produce the combined K, which could have been compared with a value of K_{IC} for a specific material.

These stress distributions, which result from different external loadings, are relatively easy to deal with because their values are usually known. Analysis becomes much more difficult when self-equilibrating, internal residual stresses, commonly introduced during welding, are encountered. In general, design stresses are easily evaluated, but residual stresses created during fabrication are much more difficult to assess because their values are not known, are not easily measured, and can be very high.

Their unknown values make the specific orientation of a crack relative to the direction of the residual stresses of secondary interest. So, being good, conservative engineers, we usually assume the worst: that the residual stresses are opening the crack, i.e. they are tensile. If residual stress distributions are of the same form, or can be assumed to be of the same form, as the external stresses, then the stresses can be added and one Y calibration curve used. Otherwise, different calibration curves are needed and the K values are added.

SAQ 1.4 (Learning outcomes 1.5 and 1.7)

The cracked pipe in SAQ 1.3 was made from steel with a yield stress of 400 MPa. It was pre- and post-weld heat treated, so tensile residual welding stresses of about 20% of yield might also be present and opening the crack. Calculate the crack-driving force K_I in the presence of both design and residual stresses; again, do this longhand.

SAQ 1.4 shows how residual stresses can affect fracture processes, if they add to an existing tensile stress to increase K_I.

The industrial terminology for the design stresses is *primary* stresses, and for the welding residual stresses that act over a short distance it is *secondary* stresses.

In addition to the significant uncertainties introduced by residual stresses, there is great potential for introducing further uncertainty when crack lengths are considered – after all, we didn't deliberately introduce the confounded things!

2.3.4 *Crack length*

The length of the crack is denoted by a in the fracture mechanics equation. Given that parts aren't deliberately manufactured with cracks in them, their size, therefore, is measured by some non-invasive process such as radiography or ultrasonics, is assumed as part of a design process, or is seen after a part has failed. In some cases the presence of a crack is assumed even if none is detected by inspection. For a safety-critical part, if a detection system that can measure cracks down to 2 mm is used and no crack is found, then assuming there are cracks of 2 mm present, which have only just been missed, is only prudent.

Crack lengths in the handbooks of Y calibrations are always regular geometries, such as semi-circles, ellipses, lines or circles. In practice, cracks are irregular and so one makes conservative assumptions about their shape. For example, if an embedded crack is triangular you might model it as a circle that envelops the triangle – particularly if you happened to have a Y calibration curve for an embedded, circular crack.

Cracks that are introduced during the fabrication of welded structures can also grow by fatigue in structures that are cyclically loaded.

Fracture mechanics comes into its own when a crack is found. Does one:

- stop the plant immediately
- order the crack ground out and rewelded (then worry about whether this has made the problem better or worse because of what it might have done to the residual stresses and the material properties)
- run the plant at a lower loading until the part can be replaced
- tell the plant manager that it is OK to keep running the plant without any remedial action and risk having to explain to the judge why it was a good decision, despite the explosion having killed the maintenance engineer?

LEFM calculations that show a good safety factor are fine for these types of problem because they are the lowest energy failure. If a failure under load were to occur not by brittle fracture but by ductile tearing mechanisms, then the calculation will simply give an extra margin for safety.

Keeping heavily loaded, cracked plant and aeroplanes in operation requires the active management of cracks using non-destructive inspection techniques. However, inspection cannot be performed in a simple 'Is there a crack there and, if there is, how big is it and what do we do about it?' sort of way. For example, a typical story (taken from the power-generation industry) runs like this:

- We haven't found any cracks on inspection, so let's assume that we could have found any and all cracks longer than 6 mm (this was the standard figure in the industry at the time, although improved NDT techniques now reduce this figure).
- So, we will assume there is a crack that is 6 mm long, which we haven't found, and that it is in the worst place, i.e. loaded by the maximum opening stress amplitude.

- We know our loading cycles exactly, and so can estimate that a 6 mm crack, if one exists, will grow by fatigue to 8 mm in a year.

- We also calculate that the crack has to grow to 16 mm before the (conservative) LEFM theory says that catastrophic failure will occur and the whole shooting match blows up and kills everyone in the building.

- So, we will inspect every year and have a safety factor of two on the critical crack length, or whatever seems comfortable.

Now comes the brilliant bit.

- After a year, we reinspect and can't find a crack, so there never was a 6 mm crack and it hasn't grown to 8 mm as estimated.

- So, the clock starts again, assuming that a 6 mm crack has just been missed; and if this cycle carries on the plant can run for ever.

- Five years down the line the NDE industry guarantees (in writing, and on the back of their insurance certificate) that with their new kit they can find all cracks over 3 mm.

- They find one 3 mm long and call it 'Sally'.

- Running the (conservative) calculations again we work out that it will take 5 years for the 3 mm crack to grow to 8 mm, based on a safety factor of 2.

- After another couple of years Sally is still 3 mm long so they time the NDE to coincide with the repainting schedule, which costs £20k, and they have to remove some paint to do the NDE anyway.

- Fifteen years down the line Sally is still 3 mm long and so the failure-assessment process clock is still reset to zero at regular intervals.

This is the key to what fracture mechanics provides: a means of assessing whether or not a crack is *safe*.

If a crack is found in a structure, then the possible courses of action (which include the sort of fracture mechanics assessment just outlined) can be constrained by the context of the problem: see the input ☑ **Cracking in nuclear plant** ☑.

2.3.5 Review of the parameters

- K_{IC} is measured in your own laboratory, bought from a test-house, guessed from experience or converted from Charpy values.

- Y is looked up in a handbook of common geometries or calculated using an FE program. I have given you a calculator on the DVD that contains the Y values that you will need during this course (more on this later).

- σ is the far-field stress calculated from a mechanics equation, looked up in a handbook or calculated numerically (in fracture mechanics there are *no* stress concentration factors calculated from the presence of the crack!).

- a is measured or estimated; pay for non-destructive evaluation/testing (NDE/NDT), and assume they have only found all cracks of the length they have written into the contract and that there is one that is just a tiny bit smaller that they haven't found.

☑ Cracking in nuclear plant

At the time of writing there are significant cracking problems at British Energy's Hunterstone B and Hinkley Point B advanced gas-cooled nuclear reactors that have been operating for over 200 000 h. The component most affected is called a bifurcation, a junction between two curved pipes within the heat-exchanger circuit, of which there are 528 per reactor.

Crack measurement by eddy-current testing (not an easy business, see Figure 1.25) reports a typical crack growth rate of 0.1 to 0.2 mm per year – although some have grown 1 mm per year.

Figure 1.25   Inspection of the heat exchanger of a nuclear reactor

This particular context, of the nuclear industry, is illustrated by this extract from an article quoting Andy Spurr (British Energy's chief technical officer):

> Spurr said that the vast majority of cracks are too insignificant to warrant repair and the rest are treated using one of four options:
>
> - Remelt affected area.
> - Replace the bifurcation.
> - Internal plugging.
> - External plugging.
>
> The chosen option depends on the particular crack and bifurcation. Spurr said that plugging is not an attractive option because it can lead to the degradation of the boiler's surface area. However, each boiler can accommodate 'quite a lot of plugging' before there is any reduction in output. Asked whether replacement of the boilers was an option, Spurr said it was highly unlikely as it would be 'practically, very, very difficult to execute.'
>
> 'British Energy's bifurcation blues' (2006) *Nuclear Engineering International*, 22 November.
> http://www.neimagazine.com/storyprint.asp?sc=2040465

3 LINEAR-ELASTIC FRACTURE MECHANICS IN PRACTICE

LEFM theory is useful notwithstanding that most overload fractures in engineering metal parts will not be brittle. If you can show that a crack in a part will not grow by fast, brittle fracture, then any plasticity involved in the fracture process will make it more difficult for the crack to grow, effectively providing an added safety factor. So, a satisfactory safety case based on an LEFM analysis means that the practitioner may not need to go any further, even though the eventual failure will not be brittle.

In this section you will practise using the fracture mechanics equation in ways that are used in industry and with issues that are important to industry.

DVD

The 'K calculator' is in the computer-based activities section of the DVD.

ACTIVITY 1: USING THE *K* CALCULATOR WORKBOOK

Open the *K* calculator; you will see a spreadsheet for entering variables into the fracture mechanics equation. You have already seen that the 'Brittle fracture' sheet has an interface for inputting variables and a drop-down menu for choosing the *Y* calibration curve appropriate to a particular geometry and loading. Now choose the 'Plate in tension – through-thickness edge crack' geometry from the drop-down menu. What you should see is shown in Figure 1.26.

Figure 1.26   The 'Brittle fracture' interface for an edge-cracked plate in tension

You can choose from four different types of calculation by using the 'radio buttons' highlighted in Figure 1.26. Try the different radio buttons and you will see different data boxes highlighted in purple. These purple boxes are where you put data in and the values in the white boxes are calculated by the spreadsheet.

These calculations happen automatically for three of the radio buttons, but the critical crack length button has an additional purple 'Calculate' button, which you must click on in order to trigger a solution.

The first radio button calculates K_I and shows the value of Y for variations in a, W and stress. If K_{IC} is given a value, then it also calculates a reserve factor on load (which is the ratio of K_{IC} to K_I).

EXAMPLE

Try putting in the values from SAQ 1.3 of stress = 180 MPa, W = 10 mm and a = 2.5 mm. Leave the fracture toughness of the material box empty. Does the answer match your answer to SAQ 1.3?

SOLUTION

The calculator is a little better at reading graphs than I am. It gives a K of 23.94 MPa √m and returns a value for Y of 1.5 (Figure 1.27). Good enough, I reckon.

Plate in tension - through-thickness edge crack

Calculate:
- ⦿ KI
- ◯ Critical crack length
- ◯ Critical stress
- ◯ KIC

Material properties:
K_{IC}: _____ MPa √m

Geometry dimensions:
Width (W): 10.000 mm
Crack length (a): 2.500 mm
Y: 1.50

Loading:
Stress: 180.00 MPa
K_I: 23.94 MPa √m
Reserve factor on the load: 0.00

Figure 1.27   Plate in tension with a through-thickness edge crack – $K_I \approx 24$ MPa √m and $Y = 1.5$

EXAMPLE

Now input a value of K_{IC}, to find one that will return a reserve factor on the load of 2.

SOLUTION

As you might expect, a K_{IC} of double the value of K_I does the trick (Figure 1.28).

Material properties:
K_{IC}:   48.00 MPa √m

Geometry dimensions:
Width (W):   10.000 mm
Crack length (a):   2.500 mm
Y: 1.50

Loading:
Stress: 180.00 MPa
K_I: 23.94 MPa √m
Reserve factor on the load: 2.00

Figure 1.28   Plate in tension with a through-thickness edge crack – the reserve factor is 2 when $K_{IC} \approx 48$ MPa √m

Now click the 'Critical crack length' radio button, which brings up the additional 'Calculate' button. Given a value for W, a K_{IC} for the material and an applied stress, this calculates the critical crack length at which brittle fracture will occur.

EXAMPLE

For the bar in Exercise 1.6, where $W = 10$ mm, and a stress of 180 MPa, determine the critical crack length if the toughness of the material is 100 MPa √m.

Hint: remember to hit 'Enter' after adding each value and then to click on 'Calculate'.

SOLUTION

The calculator gives a critical crack length of 6.0 mm.

EXERCISE 1.7

Assume now that there may be some lower-toughness weld metal in the pipe, so the crack could find itself in material with a toughness of 40 MPa √m.

Do you expect the critical crack length to cause failure to be longer or shorter? Use the calculator to produce a value.

3.846mm

Let's turn now to the 'Critical stress' radio button. If I know the crack length, the geometry and the material toughness, then I can calculate the stress that would cause brittle failure.

EXAMPLE

Still working on the edge-crack geometry, put a tiny crack into the 10 mm section and a reasonable toughness value for a steel. What is the stress that would cause brittle failure?

SOLUTION

I put in 100 MPa $\sqrt{m}$ for the toughness and 0.1 mm for the crack length, which produces a stress of 5043 MPa (Figure 1.29)!

Figure 1.29 Plate in tension with a through-thickness edge crack – the critical stress is 5043 MPa

Well, if you can produce a steel with a toughness of 100 MPa $\sqrt{m}$ and a yield stress of about 5000 MPa, it's about time to consider retiring rich. Any real steel would have yielded way before brittle failure could take place. The calculation is correct in so far as it goes, but *it doesn't address failure by any mechanisms other than brittle fracture* – I shall return to this issue later in the block.

Finally, the radio button labelled K_{IC} allows you to calculate the fracture toughness of a material from the conditions that were in place when brittle fracture took place. This is particularly useful for forensic engineering. If you have an obviously brittle fracture surface and know the loadings on the part that broke, then you have, in effect, a toughness test.

EXAMPLE

Keep using the through-thickness edge crack calibration.

If you have a broken aluminium part that has failed in a brittle fashion at a crack length of 1 mm in a 10 mm section at a nominal stress of 90 MPa, what is the fracture toughness of the material?

SOLUTION

I get a fracture toughness of about 6.0 MPa √m (Figure 1.30). This is a very low value of toughness that should appeal to the Sherlock Holmes in you: perhaps there are some other loadings or the part has been improperly used?

Figure 1.30   Plate in tension with a through-thickness edge crack – the fracture toughness of the material is approximately 6.0 MPa √m

3.1 Applying fracture mechanics

What now follows is a series of exercises and SAQs that form a design narrative. Work through these using the *K* calculator. I will draw out the key concepts as the narrative progresses.

At the heart of the design of a chemical plant is a steel, thin-walled pressure vessel that is fabricated by welding. It is a safety-critical design that has the facility for an emergency shut-down by being flooded with cold water. The emergency shut-down procedure generates long-range thermal stresses that act in the same way as the stresses generated by the pressure in the vessel, i.e. over the whole of the structure. In addition, there are welding residual stresses that act over a short range, a few millimetres around the weld, and that are self-equilibrating. The issues I am introducing here are significant to such a design, they are not simply examples to provide practice – although they do this as well.

Imagine that you are the plant designer concerned with the structural integrity of a thin-walled pressure vessel where chemical reactions take place under pressure. The high-quality steel plate from which the vessel will be made is well characterized and it is 16 mm thick. You know that its toughness on the ductile upper shelf is 140 MPa √m and on the brittle lower shelf it is 80 MPa √m, and that the transition temperature is somewhere between 0 and 10 °C. The tensile membrane stress in the vessel during normal, high-temperature operation is 300 MPa and the NDE procedures will guarantee finding all surface-breaking cracks above 4 mm in length.

EXERCISE 1.8

What will be the reserve factor on load during normal high-temperature operation of your design? Use the higher toughness value.

EXERCISE 1.9

The vessel is flooded with cold water on emergency shut-down, which induces a thermal shock loading that effectively increases the operating stress by 50%. Is the vessel still safe? (You can assume that the thermal stresses just add to the tensile membrane stress, so the same calibration factor can be used; and again, use the higher toughness value.)

So far the analysis has used the upper-shelf toughness value. If you don't know whether the steel is on the lower shelf when flooded with cold water on emergency shut-down, then unless the toughness at this temperature can be ascertained, or measured, you must use the conservative value of 80 MPa √m, i.e. the lower-shelf toughness. This reduces the reserve factor on load to an unacceptable level of just above unity (Figure 1.31), which doesn't allow much room for errors and unknowns. So this calculation is somewhat worrying.

SAQ 1.5 (Learning outcomes 1.6, 1.8 and 1.9)

You have paid for an FE analysis of the thermal loading transient that shows that it is more appropriate to treat the thermal stresses as bending stresses. How does this affect the result of your analysis?

(Hint: you will have to use more than one of the calculator load models, and add the K values by hand – the calculator won't do this for you.)

Now, a very important factor in the development of a safety case for a pressure vessel is the possible residual stresses within it. Every pressure vessel will have a weld of some sort associated with it, whether as part of the fabrication of the vessel itself, or the connection of pipework associated with the addition and removal of the vessel's contents.

Figure 1.31   The effect on the reserve factor of using the lower toughness value

You need to redo the safety case, taking into consideration the probable tensile residual stresses due to welding; the assumption is that the residual stresses act in concert with the loading stresses and with the thermal stress to open a possible crack. The yield stress of the material is 500 MPa. As a rule of thumb you can assume that if the weld is pre- and post-weld heat-treated to high standards there might still be residual stresses that are 20% of yield present. If the weld has not been heat-treated, the regulators require you to assume a worst case, i.e. that the residual stresses are equal to the yield stress of the material.

You will need to analyse the design under both assumptions. So far we have calculated that the K due to the design load is 50 MPa $\sqrt{m}$ and due to thermal shock is 18 MPa $\sqrt{m}$. The residual stress will add further to these values.

SAQ 1.6 (Learning outcomes 1.6–1.9)

Include the effects of residual stress in the calculation of the total K:

(a) during normal operation

(b) during thermal shock when an emergency shut-down occurs.

What do the results tell you about the operation of the design, given the toughness data for the material?

The fracture mechanics analysis suggests that your design is not robust enough to stand up to emergency shut-down. There clearly needs to be some amendment to the design of the vessel.

SAQ 1.7 (Learning outcomes 1.9 and 1.10)

Suggest at least two possible changes to the design of the vessel that will mean it can be constructed and operated safely.

If your NDE contractor buys a new piece of kit that can guarantee to find flaws over 3 mm long, is this the salvation of your design?

SAQ 1.8 (Learning outcomes 1.6–1.10)

Redo the calculations using a flaw size of 3 mm. Can the vessel now be operated safely:

(a) without weld heat treatment

(b) with weld heat treatment?

Neither of the reserve factors calculated in SAQ 1.8 inspires confidence, so I'm afraid you will have to increase the wall thickness to avoid potential brittle failure. Life would also be much easier if the material were on the upper shelf at 0 °C, so perhaps you should contact the steel supplier?

What you should know and be able to do so far

You have used the K calculator workbook extensively for analysing various inputs to a typical design problem. The workbook compares calculated values of K_I with the fracture toughness K_{IC}, and the difference gives a safety factor in terms of a reserve factor on load. You should now be confident in calculating safety factors in structures loaded by primary and secondary stresses using the K calculator, or longhand using Y calibrations and the fracture mechanics equation.

One of the key skills in analysing engineering problems is the ability to make appropriate simplifications. One of the aims of the design narrative you have just followed has been to introduce you to a sequence of steps where simplifications are necessary to obtain a solution simply. You must be prepared to make simplifications in order to solve a problem.

3.2 Plastic collapse

I shall now introduce one of the most important lessons in the understanding and use of LEFM: that it is possible to use the theory outside its applicability, and so make mistakes.

Consider the design of the plant that we followed through the previous section. The nominal design stress is 300 MPa and the thermal stresses are 150 MPa, giving a total of 450 MPa, which is a gnat's whisker away from the material's yield stress of

500 MPa. A structure experiencing two-thirds of the yield stress is considered to be a highly loaded structure, and this is 90% of yield.

So, could your design fail by yielding? Certainly it could.

EXERCISE 1.10

Use the K calculator to calculate the critical stress for your 3 mm edge crack.

If the stress in the whole of the wall thickness exceeds the yield stress of the material, then your design will fail by plastic collapse. So, for a 3 mm crack the whole of the wall thickness will exceed the yield stress of the material and fail by plastic collapse, long before brittle failure. Of course it won't literally collapse: it will blow up (think of bubble gum), but 'plastic collapse' is the proper term for this type of failure.

Plastic collapse is the other end of the failure spectrum to LEFM. Bend a piece of wire, such as a paper clip, a small amount and it springs back elastically. Bend it a lot and it remains permanently bent because the cross section has become plastic. Plastic collapse of a cracked body can occur without crack growth; the presence of a crack simply reduces the cross section. When the ligament has gone permanently plastic no further increase in load can be supported.

Figure 1.32 shows a bar containing an edge crack, subject to a tensile load. Now, although you can use the K calculator to assess whether the applied stress will cause the crack to grow, leading to brittle failure, let's not forget that the material might yield long before that happens. The effective area of the bar is decreased by the presence of the crack, so raising the stress on the remaining ligament. When yield is reached the bar will undergo plastic collapse.

For this geometry I can calculate the load at which plastic collapse occurs:

$$F_{crit} = B(W - a)\sigma_{yield}$$

And, using this idea, I can analyse our plant design to understand its potential for failure by plastic collapse.

The nominal hoop stress at which plastic collapse occurs in our pressure vessel is simply the yield stress of the material factored by the reduction in cross section, a/W. You can think of this in terms of the forces being carried in the wall of the vessel and the areas they act over. The overall force carried will not change, so a reduction in area just increases the stress proportionately.

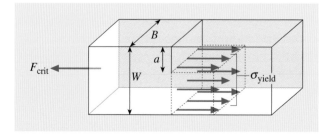

Figure 1.32   Edge-cracked bar under a tensile load

EXERCISE 1.11

If a section with a 3 mm crack yields because of the hoop stress, what is the average stress in an uncracked section? Remember that the yield strength of our material is 500 MPa.

If a cracked section were to yield at a nominal stress of 400 MPa, this gives a reserve factor of 400/300 ≈ 1.3. (The design stress is 300 MPa, remember.)

Based on what you have been doing so far, as an extension to our case study we should consider plastic collapse under the combined loading of the design stresses and the thermal shock stresses, which are in bending.

Our two simple theories, i.e. of brittle fracture and plastic collapse, operate completely independently of each other. The two material properties of K_{IC} and σ_{yield} are independent for any size of section. They are extremes of failure behaviour that do not, in themselves, define their sphere of applicability.

In industry it is routine for engineering analyses to be performed numerically on a computer, using FE analyses. The analyses of important engineering shapes and materials are captured in handbooks and data sheets, so every problem does not require a special solution. The engineering practice of solving for plastic collapse loads for cracked geometries is also supported by solutions in handbooks of common geometries. As with LEFM, if you cannot find a solution in a handbook then you have to buy a specific solution from an FE jockey.

4 SUMMARY

You know now that fracture mechanics is a useful and necessary tool for establishing the safety of structures that may undergo brittle failure if a relatively small flaw combines with high in-service loadings and residual stresses.

I have already mentioned that cracks can extend in service because of fatigue, where cyclic stresses lead to cycling of the stress intensity K. Fortuitously, it turns out that the growth of fatigue cracks can be expressed in terms of the range of K experienced by a crack as it cycles from the minimum to the maximum stress. Part 2 of this block covers the topic of fatigue in more detail, and so that is where we will continue this aspect of the application of LEFM.

LEFM breaks down if there is a lot of plasticity associated with the crack, which is hardly surprising for a theory based on linear-elasticity! Elastic–plastic fracture mechanics (EPFM) lies between the regimes of plastic collapse and LEFM. This is the subject of Part 5 of this block. EPFM is a useful and necessary tool for situations where there is too much plasticity for LEFM to be valid and not enough to cause plastic collapse. It is a complex melange of possible physical events that depends critically on the material, its state, and the geometry of the component. An elastic–plastic numerical analysis is required to solve practical problems in the EPFM regime. In Part 5 you will see enough theoretical discussion to understand the limitations of the approaches and be shown practical EPFM at a level used in current industrial practice.

Fortunately, fracture mechanics in industry combines numerical analyses of EPFM with the more straightforward plastic collapse and LEFM principles to produce a master curve that creates a failure assessment diagram (FAD) that bridges across from LEFM through EPFM to plastic collapse. In Part 5 you will study the theory and practice of EPFM using a state-of-the-art FAD, and emerge equipped to live with cracks.

LEARNING OUTCOMES

After you have studied Block 2 Part 1 you should be able to do the following.

1.1 Explain the meaning of 'plane strain' in the context of fracture toughness, and calculate whether a test sample's dimensions allow for a valid measurement to be made.

1.2 Define the key parameters in the fracture toughness equation.

1.3 Explain that Y varies as a crack grows through a component.

1.4 Calculate values of Y from calibration curves or equations.

1.5 Calculate values of K in components, given appropriate data.

1.6 Assess whether the value of K in a component, from the applied load or stress, is likely to cause brittle failure in the presence of a particular crack.

1.7 Include the likely effects of residual stress in fracture mechanics calculations.

1.8 Assess the overall contributions of K values from different sources of stress.

1.9 Use fracture mechanics concepts in the analysis of components where cracks may be present.

1.10 Describe the importance of NDE/NDT in providing data for fracture mechanics assessments.

1.11 Describe the difference between a brittle and a ductile fracture.

ANSWERS TO EXERCISES

EXERCISE 1.1

Recall from Block 1 that the maximum principal stresses lie at 45° to a state of pure shear (see Figure 1.33) – sketch a Mohr's circle if you need convincing!

Figure 1.33   Principal stress direction

EXERCISE 1.2

(a) (i) The 1973 study produces about 39–123 MPa √m.

    (ii) The SINTAP recommendation produces 32–100 MPa √m.

(b) From the rough-and-ready values in Table 1.1, K_{IC} for steels ranges from 40 to 200 MPa √m, so these recommendations cover about half of the range.

(c) The value would be $(30/12)^2 = 6.25$ J.

EXERCISE 1.3

(a) Referring back to Figure 1.8, $Y = 1$ and, by convention, the length of a surface-breaking flaw is $2a$.

(b) Referring back to Figure 1.9, $Y = 1.12$ and, by convention, the length of a surface-breaking flaw is a.

EXERCISE 1.4

(a) At an a/W of 0.25, Y is about 1.5.

(b) (i) At an a/W of 0.5, Y is about 2.8, an 87% increase.

    (ii) At an a/W of 0.75, Y is about 7.3, a 387% increase.

EXERCISE 1.5

The bending stresses go from tension to an equal magnitude of compression (Figure 1.34). The tension stresses are uniform over the depth of the section. So, the combined stress distribution varies from $\sigma_{\text{tension}} + \sigma_{\text{bending}}$ at one surface to $\sigma_{\text{tension}} - \sigma_{\text{bending}}$ at the other surface, where:

$$\sigma_{\text{tension}} = \frac{F}{A} = \frac{F}{BW}$$

and

$$\sigma_{\text{bending}} = \frac{My}{I} = \frac{\pm M\left(W/2\right)}{\left(BW^3/12\right)}$$

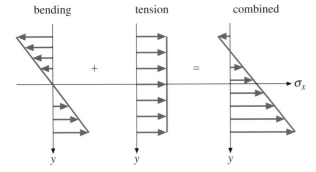

Figure 1.34   Combined stresses under bending and tension

EXERCISE 1.6

I don't need to know the cross section of the specimen in order to evaluate Y, as the Y calibrations are given in terms of a/W. I have already read off Y for $a/W = 0.25$ as about 1.5 in tension and about 1.1 in bending.

The crack length is 7.5 mm (a quarter of 30 mm).

$$K_{I_{\text{tension}}} + K_{I_{\text{bending}}} = Y\sigma_{\text{tension}}\sqrt{\pi a} + Y\sigma_{\text{bending}}\sqrt{\pi a}$$

$$K_{I_{\text{combined}}} = 1.5 \times 100 \text{ MPa} \times \sqrt{\pi\left(0.0075 \text{ m}\right)} + 1.1 \times 100 \text{ MPa} \times \sqrt{\pi\left(0.0075 \text{ m}\right)}$$

$$K_{I_{\text{combined}}} = 40 \text{ MPa} \sqrt{\text{m}}$$

EXERCISE 1.7

In a material of lower toughness, brittle failure would be expected to take place in the presence of a shorter crack.

Putting these numbers in gives a critical crack length of approximately 3.8 mm (Figure 1.35).

Figure 1.35 Plate in tension with a through-thickness edge crack – the critical crack length is ~3.8 mm

EXERCISE 1.8

The K calculator gives a K_I value of about 50 MPa √m, which gives a comfortable reserve factor on load of about 2.8 (Figure 1.36).

Figure 1.36 Plate in tension with a through-thickness edge crack – the reserve factor is about 2.8

EXERCISE 1.9

The K calculator gives a K_I value of about 76 MPa √m, which reduces the reserve factor on load to about 1.9, so failure is not predicted (Figure 1.37).

Material properties:
K_{IC}:　　140.00 MPa √m

Geometry dimensions:
Width (W):　　16.000 mm
Crack length (a):　　4.000 mm
Y:　　1.50

Loading:
Stress:　　450.00 MPa
K_I:　　75.72 MPa √m
Reserve factor on the load:　　1.85

Figure 1.37　Plate in tension with a through-thickness edge crack – at $K_I \approx 76$ MPa √m the reserve factor is about 1.9

EXERCISE 1.10

A brittle failure analysis indicates a failure stress of over 1000 MPa, i.e. more than twice the yield stress of the material (Figure 1.38).

Plate in tension - through-thickness edge crack

Calculate:
◦ KI
◦ Critical crack length
⊙ Critical stress
◦ KIC

Material properties:
K_{IC}:　　140.00 MPa √m

Geometry dimensions:
Width (W):　　16.000 mm
Crack length (a):　　3.000 mm
Y:　　1.34

Loading:
Stress:　　1074.60 MPa
K_I:　　140.00 MPa √m
Reserve factor on the load:　　1.00

Figure 1.38　Plate in tension with a through-thickness edge crack – the critical stress is ~1075 MPa

EXERCISE 1.11

a/W is 3 mm/16 mm = 0.19. So the cross section of the cracked region is 81% of the normal wall area.

$$\sigma W = \sigma_{\text{yield}} (W - a)$$

$$\sigma \times 16 \text{ mm} = 500 \text{ MPa} \times (16 \text{ mm} - 3\,\text{mm})$$

$$= \frac{13 \text{ mm}}{16 \text{ mm}} (500 \text{ MPa})$$

$$\approx 400 \text{ MPa}$$

ANSWERS TO SELF-ASSESSMENT QUESTIONS

SAQ 1.1

(a) For this material:

$$2.5\left(\frac{K_Q}{\sigma_{yield}}\right)^2 = 2.5\left(\frac{32}{380}\right)^2 \text{m} = 0.018 \text{ m}$$

So a sample with a and B greater than 18 mm is needed.

(b)

Table 1.2 Specimen sizes predicted using the standard (Equation 1.3) for the steel shown in Figure 1.13

	K_{IC}	σ_{yield}	$2.5\left(\dfrac{K_{IC}}{\sigma_{yield}}\right)^2$
High temperature	153	483	0.25 m
Low temperature	41	765	0.007 m

SAQ 1.2

At an a/W of 0.25, Y is about 1.1.

At an a/W of 0.5, Y is about 1.5, a 36% increase.

At an a/W of 0.75, Y is about 3.3, a 200% increase.

SAQ 1.3

(a) The membrane stress is calculated using Equation (1.4):

$$\sigma = p\frac{r}{t} = 15 \text{ MPa}\frac{0.12 \text{ m}}{0.01 \text{ m}} = 180 \text{ MPa}$$

I estimated Y for a quarter-through-thickness crack under tension in Exercise 1.6 as 1.5.

So:

$$K_I = Y\sigma\sqrt{\pi a}$$
$$= 1.5 \times 180 \text{ MPa} \times \sqrt{\pi(0.0025 \text{ m})}$$
$$= 24 \text{ MPa } \sqrt{\text{m}}$$

(b) A K_I of 24 MPa $\sqrt{\text{m}}$ is well below the range of fracture toughnesses for steels, even old steels, given earlier. So, probably, no.

SAQ 1.4

Although both design stresses and residual stresses are tensile, and so can be added, I shall still add the K values, because it is good practice and the answers come out the same anyway. You may want to prove this to yourself.

From SAQ 1.3:

$$K_{I_{design}} = Y\sigma\sqrt{\pi a}$$
$$= 1.5 \times 180 \text{ MPa} \times \sqrt{\pi(0.0025 \text{ m})}$$
$$= 24 \text{ MPa} \sqrt{m}$$

The residual stress is 400 MPa × 20%, which is 80 MPa.

So:

$$K_{I_{residual}} = Y\sigma\sqrt{\pi a}$$
$$= 1.5 \times 80 \text{ MPa} \times \sqrt{\pi(0.0025 \text{ m})}$$
$$= 11 \text{ MPa} \sqrt{m}$$

The total crack-driving K is therefore 35 MPa √m, which is starting to approach a value of fracture toughness for older steels.

SAQ 1.5

I can reuse the 300 MPa analysis in Exercise 1.8, which gave a K of about 50 MPa √m. However, I also need to calculate a K for a 150 MPa bending stress distribution and add this K to the tension value. Using the pure bending calibration produces a K of about 18 MPa √m (Figure 1.39), so the combined K will be 18 MPa + 50 MPa = 68 MPa √m. Comparing this with the lower-shelf toughness of 80 MPa √m gives a reserve factor on load of 80/68 ≈ 1.18. Some improvement, but not much!

Figure 1.39 Edge-cracked beam in pure bending – K_I ≈ 18 MPa √m due to 150 MPa

SAQ 1.6

The additional K due to 20% of yield (100 MPa) is about 17 MPa √m (Figure 1.40) and due to 100% of yield (500 MPa) is about 84 MPa √m (Figure 1.41).

Plate in tension - through-thickness edge crack ▾

Calculate: ⦿ KI

○ Critical crack length

○ Critical stress

○ KIC

Material properties:
K_{IC}: [   ] MPa √m

Geometry dimensions:
Width (W):   16.000 mm
Crack length (a):   4.000 mm
Y: 1.50

Loading:
Stress: 100.00 MPa
K_I: 16.83 MPa √m
Reserve factor on the load: 0.00

Figure 1.40   Edge-cracked plate in tension – $K_I \approx 17$ MPa √m due to 100 MPa

Material properties:
K_{IC}: [   ] MPa √m

Geometry dimensions:
Width (W):   16.000 mm
Crack length (a):   4.000 mm
Y: 1.50

Loading:
Stress: 500.00 MPa
K_I: 84.13 MPa √m
Reserve factor on the load: 0.00

Figure 1.41   Edge-cracked plate in tension – $K_I \approx 84$ MPa √m due to 500 MPa

The crack-driving K values are resisted by material K_{IC} values of either 80 MPa √m or 140 MPa √m, depending on whether the material is on the lower or the upper shelf.

(a) The combined K values in normal operation are:

(50 + 17) MPa √m = 67 MPa √m with 20% of yield as a residual stress.

(50 + 84) MPa √m = 134 MPa √m with 100% of yield as a residual stress.

If we can assume that the material is on the upper toughness shelf during normal operation, then the reserve factors on load are:

140/67 ≈ 2.1 with 20% of yield as a residual stress.

140/134 ≈ 1.0 with 100% of yield as a residual stress.

(b) Adding the thermal shock load:

$(18 + 50 + 17)$ MPa $\sqrt{m} = 85$ MPa $\sqrt{m}$ with 20% of yield as a residual stress.

$(18 + 50 + 84)$ MPa $\sqrt{m} = 152$ MPa $\sqrt{m}$ with 100% of yield as a residual stress.

We can see from this that if the material is on the lower shelf, then failure is predicted on emergency shut-down whatever the assumption about residual stress: the total K always exceeds the lower-shelf value of 80 MPa $\sqrt{m}$.

Under emergency shut-down conditions failure will always occur if there is no heat treatment. Using 100% of yield as a residual stress gives a total K of 152 MPa $\sqrt{m}$, in excess of the upper-shelf toughness.

SAQ 1.7

The options are:

- Use a steel that always has a high value of toughness above 0 °C, combined with pre- and post-weld heat treatment to limit the residual stresses present.

- Use a thicker steel section for the vessel wall. The flaw will then give a smaller value of a/W and all the K values will be smaller.

- Use better NDT to find smaller flaw sizes.

Note that increasing the strength of the steel does not help. Remember that toughness tends to go down as strength goes up; and in any case, a higher strength may just mean higher residual stresses.

SAQ 1.8

(a) The worst case is a design stress of 300 MPa in tension, a thermal shock of 150 MPa in bending and a residual stress of 500 MPa in tension.

With a 3 mm crack these produce K values of 39 MPa $\sqrt{m}$, 15 MPa $\sqrt{m}$ and 65 MPa $\sqrt{m}$ respectively: a total of 119 MPa $\sqrt{m}$. This squeezes under the upper-shelf toughness, but still exceeds the lower-shelf toughness.

(b) With weld heat treatment the loading is a design stress of 300 MPa in tension, a thermal shock of 150 MPa in bending and a residual stress of 100 MPa in tension (20% of the yield stress).

With a 3 mm crack these produce K values of 39 MPa $\sqrt{m}$, 15 MPa $\sqrt{m}$ and 13 MPa $\sqrt{m}$ respectively: a total of 67 MPa $\sqrt{m}$. This clears both the upper-shelf toughness and the lower-shelf toughness, giving reserve factors on load of $140/67 = 2.1$ and $80/67 = 1.2$ respectively.

ACKNOWLEDGEMENTS

Grateful acknowledgement is made to the following sources:

FIGURES

Figure 1.1: Courtesy of US National Transport Safety Bureau.

Figure 1.12: Photograph taken from Accident Investigation Report 9/78, Boeing 707 321C G-BEBP. Department of Trade Accidents Investigation Branch © Crown copyright. Reproduced with the permission of the Controller of HMSO and Queen's Printer for Scotland.

Figure 1.25: Provided by British Energy.

COURSE TEAM ACKNOWLEDGEMENTS

This part was prepared for the course team by Adrian Demaid.

PART 2
FATIGUE

CONTENTS

1 INTRODUCTION   **65**

1.1   Fatigue and its effects   65

1.2   The history of fatigue   72

1.3   Mechanisms of fatigue   73

2 FATIGUE BEHAVIOUR OF MATERIALS   **76**

2.1   The 'S–N' curve: stress–life testing   77

    2.1.1   Test-pieces and test methods   82

    2.1.2   Specimen-size effects   85

    2.1.3   Effect of surface condition   86

    2.1.4   Environmental effects   88

    2.1.5   Microstructural effects   89

2.2   Strain–life testing   89

3 USING FATIGUE DATA IN DESIGN   **92**

3.1   Stress lifing: designing for infinite life   93

3.2   Strain lifing: designing for a finite life   98

4 APPLYING FRACTURE MECHANICS TO FATIGUE   **101**

4.1   The application of linear-elastic fracture mechanics to fatigue   103

4.2   Using the Paris law   107

4.3   Practical fatigue analysis   111

4.4   Linking initiation and propagation   120

5 A PRACTICAL EXAMPLE: THE MARKHAM DISASTER   **123**

6 SUMMARY: FATIGUE DESIGN   **125**

LEARNING OUTCOMES   **126**

ANSWERS TO EXERCISES   **127**

ANSWERS TO SELF-ASSESSMENT QUESTIONS   **130**

REFERENCES   **136**

ACKNOWLEDGEMENTS   **137**

1 INTRODUCTION

1.1 Fatigue and its effects

Up to now in this course I have talked primarily about structures subjected to static loading. Designing against failure has meant that we want to avoid excessive loads that would exceed the strength of the material, or the rapid extension of a crack when the applied stress intensity reaches a critical level.

But in reality few, if any, load-bearing structures carry truly constant loads. In practice, structures may experience *cyclic loading* conditions, where the loads change with time. Under such conditions it is possible for cracks to initiate and grow, even if the stresses never exceed those caused by the design loads.

This is the phenomenon known as *fatigue*. Fatigue cracks can eventually grow long enough to cause the structure to fail. This occurs when the peak cyclic load is of sufficient magnitude to generate a stress intensity at the crack tip that exceeds the material's fracture toughness.

Failure of components and structures under cyclic loading is very common. A frequently quoted figure is that fatigue accounts for at least 90% of all service failures due to mechanical causes, although that's impossible to quantify with any real accuracy, of course. Certainly fatigue failures can be extremely costly, as can the inspection and component replacement schedules needed to ensure that they do not occur.

Cyclic or oscillating loads will not always lead to failure by fatigue. If the load variation is very small, then fatigue is less likely. When the consequences of failure would be severe, either in financial cost or human suffering, engineers take care to design components or structures to resist fatigue. This is achieved either by ensuring the loads and the load variations are low enough never to initiate fatigue cracks, or by removing the cracked part from service before the crack is long enough to cause failure. We shall study methods for designing against fatigue later in this part.

When failures do occur, the lessons learned are usually incorporated into future design processes. However, fatigue failure is not disastrous for many components and devices, and so fatigue in such components is relatively commonplace. Within our daily lives there is a host of examples of components that are subjected to cyclic loading and that fail unexpectedly, despite having been operating without showing any visible sign of anything untoward: kettle switches, door locks and handles, food mixers, laptop hinges, corkscrews, squash rackets and the hub of a bicycle wheel – and these are just from my own recent experience. You may also have had experience of something 'just falling apart in your hand'!

▽ **Failure and cracking due to fatigue** ▽ illustrates failures that have occurred as a consequence of fatigue that are all in my direct experience. The examples shown in this input are fairly mundane, and caused only mild irritation when the failure occurred. But, as noted earlier, when the component is part of a more crucial piece of a structure or machine, then the consequences can be rather more severe.

☑ Failure and cracking due to fatigue

The following three examples of failure and cracking can be attributed to fatigue; you may be able to relate to these.

The first, shown in Figure 2.1, is the fracture of a plastic WC cistern handle, which parted company from the main body without warning. There was no evidence that a crack had been propagating during use. Notice the very smooth fatigue and fracture surfaces. Such a smooth surface is one of the characteristics of a fatigue failure. The fatigue crack itself grows with no bulk plasticity (although there is local plasticity associated with its growth, as you

will see later). The final failure can then be brittle, as you saw in Part 1 of this block.

The second example is that of a titanium hub of a bicycle wheel, shown in Figure 2.2. The problem was discovered when the tyre began rubbing on the chain stay. Subsequent investigation revealed that a crack had propagated from one of the spoke eyelets, where a combination of tensile loading from the tension in the spoke, the cyclic stress from the rotation of the wheel and the stress concentration of the eyelet had contributed to the initiation and growth of the crack.

fracture surface

fatigue surface

(b)

(a)

Figure 2.1   (a) Fracture surface of a WC handle; (b) close-up of the failure surface

Figure 2.2   The hub of a bicycle wheel showing a fatigue crack growing from a spoke hole eyelet

The final example is that of the aluminium squash racket shown in Figure 2.3. Here, as you can see, cracks had grown from one of the stringing holes, where a combination of the bending stresses due to impact with the ball plus the string tension had contributed to the overall stress experienced by the racket. The hole has also acted as a stress concentrator, which has amplified the effect of the applied stress.

Figure 2.3   Cracks growing from a stringing hole in a squash racket

Many common examples of fatigue occur in moving machinery: for instance, shafts, axles, connecting rods, valves and springs. However, some very large structures also provide important examples: for instance, the fuselage of an aircraft and the hull of a submarine both experience cyclic loading conditions, as there is a difference in pressure between the inside and outside of the vehicle, which changes with its height (or depth). Even largely static structures such as bridges and buildings undergo cyclic loading in service according to the pattern of traffic flow and the force of the wind.

Despite the best efforts of fatigue design engineers, failure by fatigue leading to loss of life does occur occasionally: see ▽ **Some tragic consequences of fatigue** ▽.

▽ Some tragic consequences of fatigue

The De Havilland Comet disasters

The start of passenger services in jet aircraft in the late 1940s was marked by a series of inexplicable disasters. The Comet, developed by De Havilland after the Second World War, was the first commercial jetliner to initiate the service. It comprised an all-aluminium fuselage made from thin sheet riveted together, and powered by four jet engines. The fuselage was pressurized and streamlined so that it could fly at great height (over 30 000 feet), reducing air resistance and giving improved fuel economy (Figure 2.4).

Problems began as soon as it was introduced into commercial operation: two non-fatal crashes occurred due to poor aerodynamics, but this was corrected. More serious was the total loss of G-ALYV (code-named Yoke Victor), with its 43 passengers and crew, near Calcutta in a severe thunderstorm on 2 May 1953. The inquiry found that the aircraft had broken up in the storm due to a faulty tailplane, and debris was found scattered over a very wide area. However, later accidents were to suggest that the entire structure was deeply flawed.

Early the following year, on 10 January 1954, Comet G-ALYP (Yoke Peter) took off from Rome and disappeared while climbing to 25 000 feet near Etna. There were 35 victims. Three explosions were reported by witnesses on the ground. All the debris was assumed lost in the sea. The inquiry concluded that a bomb or engine failure had caused the disaster. Flights were resumed in March

Figure 2.4   One of the first Comets

after several modifications. But then disaster struck again, less than a month later (8 April 1954) under remarkably similar circumstances. G-ALYY (Yoke Yoke) took off safely from Rome, but radio contact was lost shortly after, when the plane should have been near Stromboli. There were 21 victims. Some debris was found in the sea, but heavier debris was lost in deep water.

The state of the bodies recovered supported explosive decompression as the cause of death in both Yoke Peter and Yoke Yoke.

Meanwhile detailed tests were under way. The fuselage of another Comet (G-ALYU, Yoke Uncle) was pressurized hydraulically in a water tank to simulate the effects of pressure on the structure. The fuselage failed catastrophically and unexpectedly after a low number of pressurization cycles, after cracks grew from the corners of the windows (Figure 2.5).

Furthermore, debris from G-ALYP (Yoke Peter) had by now been lifted from the sea and could be pieced together (Figure 2.6). Detailed analysis suggested

that a critical crack had initiated from a corner in a radio-aerial window on the top of the fuselage and grown longitudinally during the explosive decompression.

There were several stress concentrators acting to increase the local stress when the fuselage was under pressure. At the window corner there would be an inevitable increase in stress due to the sharp corner itself. Then there were rivet holes, and there were also small cracks produced during manufacture of the 0.6 mm thick sheet aluminium alloy. The cracks had been found and small holes drilled at their ends to stop further growth. However, small fatigue zones were found on the critical crack that pointed to an origin on a countersunk rivet hole some distance from the corner itself (Figure 2.7).

The tests on Yoke Uncle, which had already been in service, showed that the cabin had failed at a total of 3060 pressurization cycles. This was reckoned at the time to be an overestimate, equivalent to about 2500 for a cabin in service. Yoke Peter had blown apart at 1290 cycles and Yoke Yoke at only 900 cycles.

Figure 2.5   Cracks from window corners in test

Figure 2.6
Reconstruction of debris in critical zone of G-ALYP

Figure 2.7 Critical crack at edge of aerial window

Tests done before the accidents had indicated failure at a wildly optimistic 18 000 cycles, and it is interesting that these tests also resulted in fatigue failure at a window corner. Reasons for the discrepancies included that the tests had been conducted at a constant temperature, whereas real in-service cycles involved large temperature changes during ascent, and that there were variations in manufacturing quality between different aircraft.

Also, the initial tests were performed on a fuselage that had been given an overpressure proof test, i.e. at higher pressures than met in service, at up to twice the normal cabin pressure of about 60 kPa. This would affect the stress distribution around the stress-concentrating effect of the window corners, by local plastic deformation, and so subsequent fatigue tests would be invalid.

Testing should be as close as possible to real circumstances, and should make allowance for any unknowns. In other words, a larger safety factor should have been used to allow for uncertainties.

The fatigue theory was the most probable cause of failure, although one other, rejected, hypothesis suggested that a phenolic resin glue (Redux®) used for bonding some of the structural elements may have failed prematurely.

The entire Comet fleet was grounded until structural and design changes were made to the fuselage to reduce the severity of the stress raisers, to improve its integrity. The wings and engines had also suffered fatigue cracking and the designs were modified accordingly. The new aircraft re-entered service in 1958, by which time the Boeing 707 and Douglas DC-8 had already been introduced. Both could carry double the number of passengers of the Comet. The British aircraft industry never recovered the ground lost to Boeing and Douglas owing to the design flaws, but the Comet survives today as the Nimrod military surveillance aircraft.

The *Alexander L. Kielland*

The *Alexander L. Kielland* (Figure 2.8a) was a Norwegian oil platform in the Ekofisk field. The platform, located 320 km east from Dundee, was owned by the US company Phillips Petroleum. It was built between 1973 and 1976 in France to an established design. The platform was in fact never used for drilling, but served as living quarters for the crew of the *Edda* platform, located nearby. On 27 March 1980, while most of the crew were in the platform's cinema, a support bracing failed in bad weather (Figure 2.8b). There was then a series of failures of other support braces, and one of the support columns that provided buoyancy to the platform broke off. The platform capsized twenty minutes later. Of the 212 people aboard, 123 were killed. At the time of writing this is the worst disaster in Norwegian offshore history.

(a)

Figure 2.8 (a) *Alexander L. Kielland* oil platform; (b) the failed bracing with detail; (c) fatigue markings on the failed brace

weld
brace wall
weld
hydrophone assembly

cross section of the hydrophone support

fracture

(b)

(c) "beach marks"

The investigative report concluded that the platform collapsed owing to a fatigue crack in one of six bracing struts that connected a support column to the rest of the platform. The fatal fatigue crack had initiated from a weld that attached a hydrophone (an underwater microphone) to the structure. The weld was of poor quality and acted as an initiation site for a fatigue crack that grew around the wall of the bracing until final failure occurred by brittle fracture. The report also identified shortcomings in the overall design with respect to its stability and buoyancy, and there was criticism of the emergency-management procedures that were in place.

The process of fatigue can leave characteristic 'beach marks' on a fracture surface, as a result of the gradual propagation of the crack over many cycles of load and the oxidation of the crack faces during this period. The beach marks in this case can be seen on the surface of the failed part in Figure 2.8(c). Marks like this on a failure surface are one of the hallmarks of a fatigue failure. They show the area of the crack that was caused by fatigue, as distinct from the final brittle fracture.

The Eschede train disaster

The Eschede train accident has been described as the world's worst high-speed train disaster. It happened on 3 June 1998, near the village of Eschede in Lower Saxony: 101 people were killed and about 100 were severely injured. An InterCityExpress (ICE) train is shown in Figure 2.9(a).

The ICE trains were originally fitted with one-piece cast 'monoblock' wheels, but this design suffered from severe vibration at high speed. The problem was solved by fitting a steel tyre to the central wheel disc and incorporating a rubber damping ring between the wheel and the tyre (Figure 2.9b). This new design successfully reduced vibration and noise, but it was not tested comprehensively at operating speeds and loads before being put into service. Other users of this design had, in fact, identified as early as 1992 that it seemed to lead to a reduced fatigue life of the wheel.

The fatigue crack in this case initiated at the *inside* rim of the steel tyre. The inspection of wheels

(a)

axle

rubber ring

(b)

(c)

Figure 2.9   The German InterCityExpress (or ICE) high-speed train; (b) the wheel design that failed; (c) the failed wheel

traditionally looks at the outer rim, but the revised design, with the rubber spacer, allowed tensile bending stresses to develop on the inner surface of the tyre. This became worse as the tyres were reprofiled during maintenance, which • progressively reduces the thickness. With a wheel experiencing typically 500 000 revolutions per day, the possibility for the cyclic loading to cause fatigue cracking is obvious (Figure 2.9c). The tyre that failed had initially been 64 mm thick, but wear and reprofiling had reduced it to 35 mm.

SAQ 2.1 (Learning outcome 2.1)

What were the critical flaws that led to the failures by fatigue in the examples of:

(a) the Comet airliner *Stress concentrators*

(b) the *Alexander L. Kielland* platform
after hydrophone mounting

(c) the Eschede train crash?
design of wheel used

1.2 The history of fatigue

The first work on fatigue of metals is usually attributed to Wilhelm Albert (1787–1846), who worked in the German mining industry. He noticed the failure of mine chains when they were subjected to repeated loads that were relatively small, and devised a machine to test chains under these conditions (Figure 2.10).

Over the next two decades the concept of metals becoming 'tired' or 'fatigued' was proposed by engineers such as Jean-Victor Poncelet (1788–1867). The first systematic experimental study of fatigue is often attributed to Sir William Fairbairn, 1789–1874 (Figure 2.11), a Scottish engineer who correctly identified that a beam would fail if a load well below its failure load was applied and removed many times. He also discovered the important factor that <u>increasing the magnitude of the load being applied and removed reduced the number of load cycles to failure</u>:

> It is evident that wrought-iron girders, when loaded to the extent of a tensile strain of seven tons per square inch, are not safe, if the strain is subjected to alternate changes of taking off the load and laying it on again …; and what is important to notice is, that from 300,000 to 400,000 changes of this description are sufficient to ensure fracture. It must, however, be borne in mind that the beam from which these conclusions are derived had sustained upwards of 3,000,000 changes with nearly five tons tensile strain on the square inch, and it must be admitted from the experiments thus recorded that five tons per square inch of tensile strain on the bottom of girders, as fixed by the Board of Trade, appears to be an ample standard of strength.

Fairbairn (1864)

Figure 2.10   Albert's testing machine

Figure 2.11   Sir William Fairbairn (1789–1874)

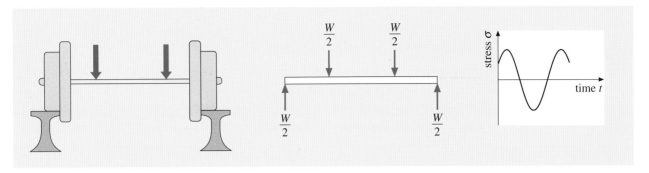

Figure 2.12 Schematic of an axle showing the applied loading

Closely following Fairbairn's research was the work of August Wöhler (1819–1914), an engineer in the German railway system. Wöhler was concerned by the failure of axles after various times in service, where the failures were occurring at much lower loads than expected.

An axle is essentially a cylindrical beam loaded in four-point bending (Figure 2.12). The top surface is in compression and the bottom surface is in tension. Rotation of the axle by a half turn leads to the top becoming the bottom and vice versa. Hence, the stresses on a particular surface region of axle vary sinusoidally between tension and compression. This is known as 'fully reversed' fatigue loading.

1.3 Mechanisms of fatigue

The use of the term 'fatigue' is a shade unfortunate, because it conjures up an image of the material actually becoming 'tired' in service; this simple analogy is a misconception. Another historical misconception was that 'fatigue is a brittle failure', because fatigue failures generally exhibit the sort of flat fracture surface typical of a brittle fracture. You can see this for yourself on the failed keyed shaft shown in Figure 2.13. A fatigue crack has grown from one edge of the key slot and penetrated about two-thirds of the way through before final ductile failure. The area of the shaft where the fatigue crack grew slowly is very flat, like a brittle fracture. The crack was in fact growing in very small plastic steps, but the deformation does not show up on the macroscopic scale.

Figure 2.13 Fracture surface of a keyed shaft; the smooth area is the fatigue surface originating from the keyway; the final ductile failure is characterized by the heavily distorted region

We will examine the actual microstructural mechanisms that lead to fatigue failure in a range of materials in Part 3 of this block. For now, it is useful if we briefly define the differences between crack *initiation* and crack *growth*.

For convenience,
I will focus this section
on the fatigue of
polycrystalline metals.
Similar effects are seen
in other materials, but
the mechanisms may be
different; I will touch on
this later in the block.

Crack initiation (also sometimes referred to as nucleation) is the formation of an initial crack. Fatigue failure does not require there to be a macroscopic defect or crack in the material in the first place. In some cases, a sharp crack may already exist in the material when it is first loaded, and then, of course, there is no crack initiation period. More often a fatigue crack will initiate at some flaw or point of stress concentration. If there are no preferential initiation sites, then cracks may form on crystallographic slip bands within the grains of the metal; as they are driven by shear stresses, these are typically at 45° to the principal stress axes. Metallurgists like to call this *Stage I* fatigue cracking, although, as it is rarely seen in engineering practice, this is not a particularly useful definition. Following initiation, the crack will grow (or *propagate*) across the body, usually perpendicular to the maximum principal stress. This stage is referred to as *Stage II* growth. Figure 2.14 illustrates this view of crack initiation and growth, the two stages involved in crack growth.

Cracks growing perpendicular to the maximum principal stress are being opened in mode I loading by that stress (recall this from Part 1: this is the same loading that is used to test K_{IC}).

The *crack initiation life* is the number of cycles it takes to produce a sharp crack. In practice, defining how long that takes depends on how carefully you look for the crack. In an electron microscope we can detect cracks only a few micrometres long, whereas on an undersea oil platform we will do well to detect a crack that is 5 mm long. (One inspection diver found a crack large enough to insert his hand into, and could feel the crack gripping and releasing his hand as the load on the structure cycled, opening and closing the crack mouth.) So, understandably, engineers use a definition of crack initiation that is dependent on the context of the fatigue problem. We shall see later, however, that the concept of crack initiation and growth is essential to fatigue design methods. One of the common descriptions of the assessment of the fatigue life of a component is that it can be assessed by summing the two contributions: the lifetime required to initiate a crack and the lifetime required to grow that crack to failure; thus:

$$N_{total} = N_{initiation} + N_{propagation}$$

Growth

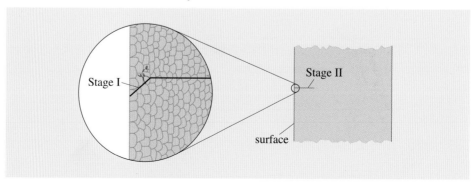

Figure 2.14   An illustration of the two stages involved in crack growth

I have already mentioned, in Part 1, that fatigue is exploited to produce a sharp crack 'to order' in specimens used for measuring the fracture toughness K_{IC}. In these specimens, controlled crack growth occurs under a cyclic stress, where the stress intensity K is kept well below the K_{IC}. Fatigue occurs at values of K that are significantly less than K_{IC} and so fatigue is often referred to as *sub-critical crack growth*.

EXERCISE 2.1

Is this concept of crack growth that occurs slowly cycle by cycle over time, at stress intensity values below K_{IC}, consistent with the ideas on the stability of cracks presented in Part 1 of this block? NO .

So, fatigue is a 'cumulative' form of failure brought about as a result of repeated cyclic loading. Quite often a single crack is the source of a failure, but, depending on the loading, many cracks may form in a component. Figure 2.15 shows a splined shaft where each spline is a stress concentrator and cracks have grown from multiple sites. This occurred because the in-service torque was increased on the component without changing its design, either by making the shaft bigger or using a more fatigue-resistant material.

Figure 2.15   Cracks grown from multiple initiation sites led to fracture of this splined shaft

2 FATIGUE BEHAVIOUR OF MATERIALS

One of the aims of this part is to introduce you to the basic characteristics of fatigue and to equip you with an understanding of the design methods needed to avoid failure by fatigue in practice.

Designing against fatigue needs not only a theoretical understanding of the fatigue process, but also data on the fatigue strength of the material under actual operating conditions. This raises a fundamental question. In many cases of fatigue it can be several years before sufficient stress cycles are accumulated to cause fatigue failure. So, do laboratory tests also need to span such a long time scale? For metals the answer is usually 'no'. The fatigue properties of metals can be determined by applying cyclic loads at much higher frequencies than would be experienced in service, without affecting the validity of the results obtained. Although the testing *time* clearly depends on the frequency of loading that is used to test the specimen, it is the number of load *cycles* that is important. Therefore, it is common to test at as high a frequency as is possible, which presents no difficulties for metals (provided time-dependent processes like corrosion or creep do not occur). However, for polymeric materials this may cause accelerated failure due to internal heating – you may have noticed how car tyres become warm in use under the cyclic loading caused by contact with the road. In carrying out accelerated laboratory tests, we must try to match the testing stresses to the service stresses.

Thus, to predict with reasonable accuracy the response and life span of a component subject to cyclic loading before putting it into service, two approaches are used:

1   Simulation of actual operating service conditions on a real or model structure.

2   Tests on standard material specimens that can then be related to service conditions.

During the last 40 years, simulation of in-service behaviour has come into prominence and in many cases now, particularly when human life is at stake, such tests are mandatory before the component or structure is allowed to go into service. Simulation tests are particularly important for civil aircraft and involve the testing to failure of components (e.g. wing panels), sub-assemblies (e.g. a wing or the fuselage, as illustrated in Figure 2.16) or even the complete aircraft.

Testing in this way provides a clear indication of the fatigue life that can be expected of the structure. It can also highlight areas where fatigue cracking is likely to occur, so that inspection regimes can be devised. It can also reveal unforeseen problems where the load paths in a structure lead to fatigue failure earlier than had been anticipated.

However, in many structures and pieces of machinery the actual cyclic loading experienced is complex and, therefore, difficult to simulate. In addition, the in-service load cycling may not be exactly what the designer had anticipated. For example, it may be that additional unexpected stresses are incorporated during assembly. In spite of these difficulties, however, simulation testing can be very informative, albeit very expensive. When simulation testing cannot be carried out, or information has to be obtained for the design of a prototype, we have to depend on fatigue data derived from laboratory tests on standard specimens.

Figure 2.16 Fatigue testing on an aircraft fuselage

2.1 The 'S–N' curve: stress–life testing

The cyclic stresses that lead to fatigue can arise either from a cyclic applied *load* or from a cyclic *strain* (or deflection). Although it might seem that a deflection has to be associated with a load, recall that thermal effects can cause strains as well.

Historically, fatigue studies have tended to be concerned with conditions of service in which failure occurred at more than 10^4 cycles of stress, so-called *high-cycle fatigue*. However, there is a wide range of engineering applications where components are subjected to large changes in stress and can experience low numbers of cycles to failure, i.e. *low-cycle fatigue*. The Comet disasters are an example of a low-cycle fatigue failure.

Figure 2.17 shows some of the possible forms of applied stress that can be produced by cyclic loading. I will use Figure 2.17 to introduce some of the essential terminology of fatigue.

Let's start with Figure 2.17(a). The stress pattern illustrated here is called an alternating stress, because the stress continuously cycles between tension and compression; this is the sort of stress experienced in a vehicle axle, as I mentioned earlier. The stress range $\Delta\sigma$ is the difference between the maximum stress σ_{max} and the minimum stress σ_{min} in a load cycle, that is:

$$\Delta\sigma = \sigma_{max} - \sigma_{min} \qquad (2.1)$$

We also need to define the mean stress σ_{m}. This is given by:

(average)

$$\sigma_{m} = \frac{\sigma_{max} + \sigma_{min}}{2} \qquad (2.2)$$

The mean stress is important: changing the mean stress will give a different fatigue life for a particular stress range. For the alternating stress pattern in Figure 2.17(a), the mean stress σ_{m} during a loading cycle is clearly zero. In Figure 2.17(b), the stress is always tensile and, hence, σ_{m} will be a net tensile stress; for this reason the stress pattern is called *fluctuating tension*.

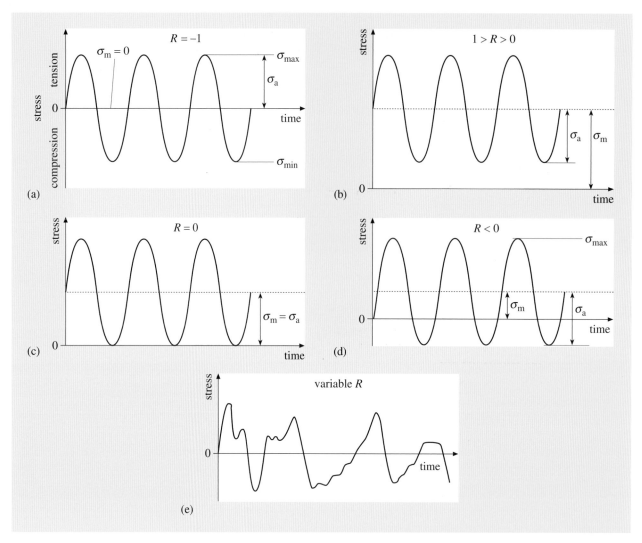

Figure 2.17   Possible forms of fatigue stress arising from cyclic loading: (a) alternating stress; (b) fluctuating tension; (c) pulsating tension; (d) fluctuating mixed; (e) random

It is customary to regard a cyclic stress as having a stress amplitude σ_a. The stress amplitude is simply half the stress range:

$$\sigma_a = \frac{\Delta\sigma}{2} \tag{2.3}$$

A uniform cyclic stress can therefore be described in terms of the stress amplitude, and the mean stress. We can also define a stress ratio R where:

$$R = \frac{\sigma_{min}}{\sigma_{max}} \tag{2.4}$$

Figure 2.17(c) shows the case where $\sigma_m = \sigma_a$, in which the minimum stress is zero.

In Figure 2.17(d), σ_{min} is compressive and σ_{max} is tensile, with σ_m also being tensile.

The purely sinusoidal stress cycles shown in Figures 2.17(a)–(d) are usually seen only in laboratory tests; the stress cycles experienced by components in service are almost invariably far more complex. Figure 2.17(e) is typical of the stress pattern found in most <u>real situations</u>, where the <u>stress is random in both amplitude and frequency</u>. An example of such a pattern might be the loading on a car's suspension as it travels over different road surfaces at different speeds.

EXERCISE 2.2

$$R = \frac{\sigma_{min}}{\sigma_{max}}$$

Determine the stress ratio R for the case when:

(a) the maximum stress is $+\sigma_a$ and the minimum stress is $-\sigma_a$ — 1

(b) the maximum stress is 200 MPa and the minimum stress is 40 MPa   0.2

(c) the maximum stress is 300 MPa and the minimum stress is 0 MPa   0

(d) the maximum stress is 200 MPa and the minimum stress is −20 MPa.   − 0.1

Q2.6.

The simplest laboratory fatigue tests are those used to obtain a so-called 'S–N fatigue curve' for a specific material, or a part, such as an aircraft skin-stringer assembly (Figure 2.18). These tests determine the number of loading cycles (the N of the section heading) that the sample survives before fracture occurs. By changing the load amplitude, the fatigue life over a range of stress amplitudes (the S of the section heading) can be determined. Typical applied-stress cycles during such a test might be as shown in Figures 2.17(a)–(c).

To generate an S–N curve, a series of samples is tested to <u>failure at a range of stress amplitudes</u>. Typically, the aim of the test is to generate fatigue lives between about 10^3 and 10^7 cycles, and the applied stress ranges will be chosen accordingly. It is rare for engineering components to experience more than 10^7 stress cycles during an operating lifetime, although there are exceptions. <u>A sample that has not failed after 10^7 cycles would be called a 'run-out' and the test halted</u>. Given that 20 Hz (i.e. 20 loading cycles per second) is a typical test frequency, a test that lasts 10^7 cycles

Figure 2.18 Fatigue testing an aircraft skin-stringer panel mock-up

will take nearly 6 days to run. Going to 10^8 cycles would, therefore, take 2 months, which will become very costly.

EXERCISE 2.3

A typical crankshaft in a car engine should survive at least 2×10^9 revolutions before failing (equivalent to about 500 000 miles, or about 805 000 km). On this basis, how long will it take a fatigue machine to break a specimen of the crankshaft material:

(a) at 1 Hz   *over 63 years.*

(b) at 100 Hz?   *231 days.*

Hz = loading cycles per second

A typical set of results from a series of S–N fatigue tests is shown in Figure 2.19. There is a very wide range of cycles to failure, so if the number of cycles to failure were plotted on a linear scale, then the data would be too closely packed to analyse effectively; therefore, a logarithmic scale is used, as shown. In this case, several samples were tested at various stress amplitudes at a stress ratio R of 0.1, i.e. the maximum stress was 10 times the minimum stress and the applied stress was always tensile. Note that testing more than once at a particular stress amplitude does not always give the same result: there is scatter in the data obtained, which simply reflects variability in the material and, probably, the surface finish of the samples. There is always an element of statistical variability in fatigue life, as no two cracks will initiate in exactly the same way or at the same rate.

Figure 2.19 shows two material conditions: peened and unpeened. As expected, the material given a shot-peening treatment to improve its fatigue life (see Block 1 Part 7) shows a greater number of cycles to failure at a given stress amplitude.

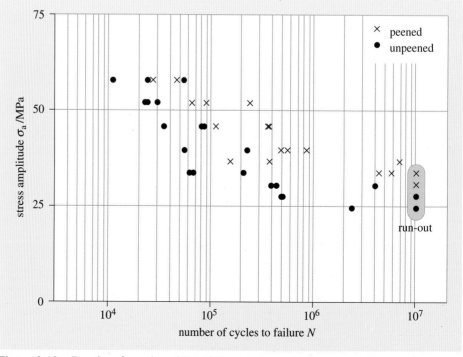

Figure 2.19   Results of a series of S–N fatigue tests on a magnesium alloy

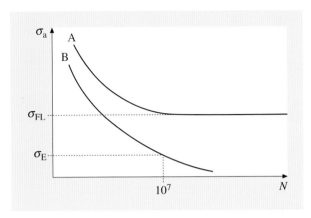

Figure 2.20 Idealized forms of the S–N curve

S–N curves tend to have two basic forms, as shown in Figure 2.20. If the S–N curve runs parallel to the N-axis at high values of N, as does curve A in Figure 2.20, then we can identify a limiting stress amplitude below which failure by fatigue does not occur, irrespective of how many stress cycles the material undergoes. This limit is called the *fatigue limit*, labelled σ_{FL}. This sort of behaviour is typical of ferritic steels (and also a few titanium alloys). As a very rough practical guide, for smooth specimens (i.e. unnotched, with no pre-existing stress concentrators), *the fatigue limit is about 40–50% of the tensile strength of such a material*.

In contrast, most non-ferrous alloys and polymeric materials exhibit an S–N curve that continues to fall gradually as the stress amplitude is lowered; curve B in Figure 2.20 is a typical example. Since the S–N curve is at no point parallel to the N-axis, these materials do not have a fatigue limit and a crack will eventually propagate to failure whatever the stress amplitude. However, in those cases, for convenience we can define an *endurance limit* σ_E as the stress amplitude at which fatigue failure will not occur after a specified number of stress cycles (e.g. $N = 10^7$ cycles) as shown in Figure 2.20.

As I mentioned previously, it is common practice to define two regimes of S–N behaviour arbitrarily:

- The first regime is known as low-cycle fatigue; in this regime failure occurs in less than about 10^4 cycles, where the stress amplitudes are large.

- The second regime is referred to as high-cycle fatigue; here, the number of cycles N exceeds 10^4 cycles and the stress amplitudes are relatively small.

Failures from high-cycle fatigue tend to be more common in practice: 10^5 cycles can be applied in just over a day with a stress cycle of 1 s, or in only a couple of minutes for the crankshaft of a car engine! On the other hand, the stresses arising from the start/stop cycle of a nuclear reactor might occur once every six months, so a lifetime of 1000 cycles might well be acceptable; this is certainly a low-cycle fatigue problem.

I must emphasize that an S–N curve is specific to a particular value of the mean stress level σ_m or the stress ratio R, and one of these should be stated on the curve. Some common tests use an alternating stress where the mean stress $\sigma_m = 0$. In general, the fatigue life will be reduced (and the curve, therefore, will be shifted downwards) by an increase in the value of σ_m, as the value of σ_{max} will increase; thus, failure will occur sooner, as K_{IC} is reached at a shorter final crack length. The fatigue limit can also disappear if the stress cycles are not of constant amplitude, e.g. if an occasional overload occurs that can initiate damage that leads to the development of a crack.

Tests at a constant, non-zero R value will have changing mean stress for different stress amplitudes, but this is realistic for many loading situations. So for $R = 0.1$, for example, a stress range of 100 MPa will be from 11 to 111 MPa with a mean stress of 61 MPa, whereas a stress range of 200 MPa will be from 22 to 222 MPa with a mean stress of 122 MPa.

EXERCISE 2.4

(a) What is the fatigue limit for the steel shown in Figure 2.21? 340 MPa

(b) What is the endurance limit for $N = 10^8$ cycles for the aluminium shown in Figure 2.21? 120 MPa

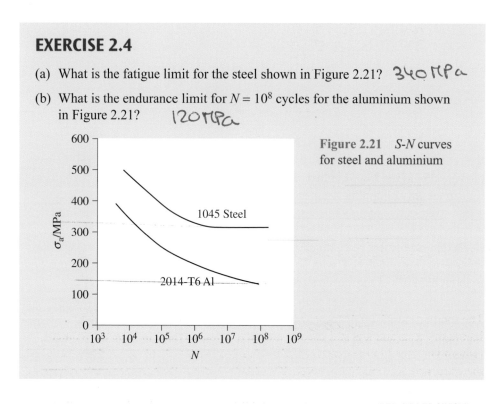

Figure 2.21 *S-N* curves for steel and aluminium

2.1.1 Test-pieces and test methods

Standard stress-cycle fatigue tests carried out in the laboratory use a range of techniques for applying the cyclic loading, such as:

axial ('push–pull')

rotating bend

cantilever bend

torsion.

Controlling the *stress* in the specimen by varying the applied load is more common than controlling the *strain*. This is partly because the measurement of strain is more difficult – requiring a transducer, such as a strain gauge, to be attached to the sample – and also because knowledge of the stress dependence of the fatigue life is needed in many (but not all) applications.

Unnotched test specimens, such as those in Figure 2.22, are often used; these have generous radii of curvature at changes of section, as well as polished surfaces, to ensure that the crack nucleation stage is not influenced by defects and stress concentrations.

$r < 6d$
d

$r < 6b$
b

(a)

(b) *Rotating cantilever beam*

(c)

(d)

Figure 2.22 Typical fatigue test-pieces: (a) axial loading; (b) rotating bend; (c) cantilever bend; (d) torsion

The rotating cantilever beam (Figure 2.22b) was the basis of one of the first laboratory tests and it is still used to this day. It was devised in 1860 by Wöhler (whom you met earlier) to test samples of railway axles. As shown in Figure 2.23(a), the specimen is rotated by a motor. Weights hung from the bearings apply a constant bending moment to a given section of the specimen. As the specimen rotates at constant speed, the point P (see Figure 2.23b) experiences a bending stress that varies sinusoidally with the angle of rotation θ (and hence with time). In this way Wöhler was able to investigate the effect of the shoulder radius on the fatigue life. His machine closely simulates the regular sinusoidal loading pattern on rotating railway axles (as shown in Figure 2.12). Modern versions of this machine are still used to generate S–N data and are particularly convenient because the specimens are easily manufactured and gripped, while the high rotational speeds used enable 10^6 or 10^7 cycles to be achieved in a relatively short time.

A more sophisticated and versatile type of test machine is the servo-hydraulic testing machine, used in mechanical testing laboratories worldwide. These machines can be used for a range of materials testing, and they are able to apply cyclic loads at high frequencies. Figure 2.24 shows a picture of a fatigue sample on such a machine. In this case the machine is used to apply a tensile load, but the machine can apply compressive loads as well. The lower actuator moves up or down; so, changing the loading jig allows different sample configurations to be tested.

The stress cycles imposed by a fatigue testing machine are usually of constant amplitude and sinusoidal, but it is possible to apply load spectra that vary in both amplitude and frequency during the test. However, bear in mind that laboratory fatigue tests are only idealized representations of what can happen in practice.

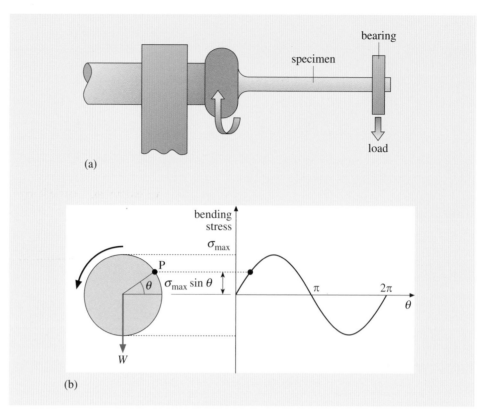

Figure 2.23   (a) A rotating cantilever beam test; (b) the change in bending stress at a point on the specimen during rotation

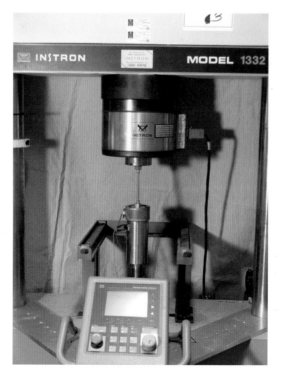

Figure 2.24   A fatigue test specimen in a servo-hydraulic fatigue testing machine

2.1.2 Specimen-size effects

Specimen-size effects are very important in fatigue. Experimental data generated from laboratory tests on small specimens can differ from those observed in the actual components or from the simulated testing of complete structures. It is now well established that larger specimens show lower fatigue or endurance limits; thus, small laboratory specimens can give artificially high values of 'safe' working stress levels that would in practice cause a 'life-size' component to break.

Figure 2.25 illustrates the magnitude of this size effect for unnotched specimens of alloy steel. Clearly, when using fatigue test data from a handbook, a designer must be very aware of all conditions under which the tests were carried out, and particularly of the specimen size.

The size effect has its origin in any or all of the following three factors:

1 A statistical size effect: the larger the specimen is, the greater the probability of a flaw existing in a highly stressed region of the specimen.

2 A microstructural size effect: the microstructure often varies with the size of the component and the position within it. The distribution of features that affect crack nucleation, such as inclusions, may vary with the size of the component.

3 A notch-size effect: the dimensions of any notch in relation to the dimensions of the component section are important. This will affect the volume of material exposed to high stress.

An example of the influence of size effects is that there is often a lack of agreement between the *S*–*N* curves determined by the rotating bend test and that determined by a geometrically different test such as the axial 'push–pull' (see Figure 2.26).

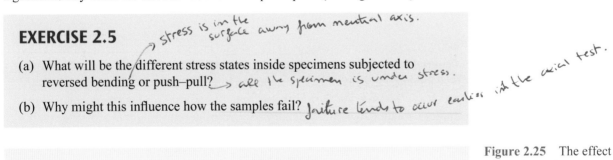

EXERCISE 2.5   *→ stress is in the surface away from neutral axis.*

(a) What will be the different stress states inside specimens subjected to reversed bending or push–pull? *→ all the specimen is under stress.*

(b) Why might this influence how the samples fail? *failure tends to occur earlier in the axial test.*

(a)   number of cycles to failure *N*

(b)   diameter/mm

Figure 2.25 The effect of specimen size: (a) changes in the *S*–*N* curve for different sample diameters; (b) changes in the fatigue strength at 10^7 cycles of an alloy steel as the sample diameter is increased

Figure 2.26 *S–N* curve for an alloy steel tested under axial loading compared with that tested in rotating bend

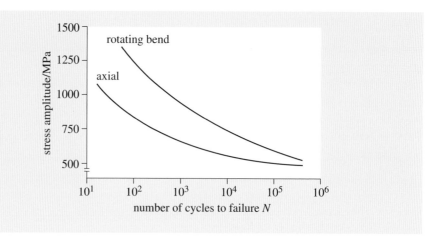

Figure 2.27 Schematic *S–N* diagram showing distribution of lives at various stress levels

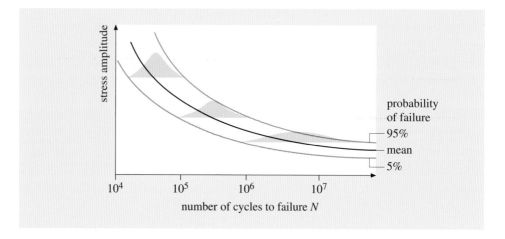

Finally, because the early stages of the fatigue process are random in nature, considerable scatter exists in experimental results. Figure 2.27 illustrates the type of distribution of lives that might be expected if many specimens were tested at each stress level: you saw the type of scatter seen in real data for the magnesium alloy samples I mentioned earlier (Figure 2.19). Some designs might acceptably use the *S–N* curve associated with, say, a 5% probability of failure; but this approach would be clearly unacceptable for a highly safety-critical component. In many cases the *S–N* data alone are not sufficient; what is needed is an understanding of how fast a crack actually grows through the material. More on this later.

2.1.3 *Effect of surface condition*

In most components fatigue cracks propagate from a surface, so the surface condition will have a profound effect on fatigue strength and life. Roughness, porosity and inclusions, such as slag or oxide particles, can all reduce the fatigue life, because they introduce sites from which a fatigue crack can initiate. Figure 2.28 shows schematically the effect of the surface condition on the fatigue limit. Polishing a sample provides the best fatigue life; a machined finish or a sharp notch reduces it. The sensitivity to surface condition increases as the static tensile strength of the material increases; this is due to an effect called ☑ **notch sensitivity** ☑.

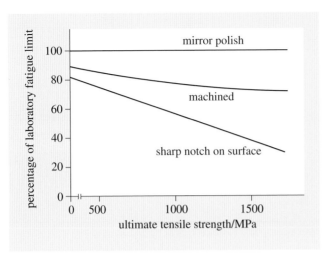

Figure 2.28 The effect of surface condition and strength on the fatigue limit

The fatigue performance of components can be enhanced by ensuring that they have smooth, preferably polished, surfaces. But for most products such a good surface finish is either not feasible or not practicable, and even if it can be achieved it is difficult to maintain. However, in some crucial applications, such as in high-performance machinery, surface polishing is used, e.g. the connecting rods in racing-car engines. And you have already seen how residual stress can be introduced into a surface to act against the stresses that would cause fatigue.

☑ Notch sensitivity

You will recall from Block 1 that a <u>notch is a stress concentrator; so are defects such as scratches and inclusions.</u> You may also have noticed that, when talking about fatigue testing, I have been careful to refer to the specimens as being 'unnotched'.

Figure 2.29 shows an example of how the *S–N* curve of a smooth component is lowered significantly by the presence of a moderate notch (where the stress concentration factor $\alpha_k = 1.76$). (Note that here I am using the α symbol for a stress concentration, not K as in Block 1; this is to avoid confusion with the use of K for stress-intensity factor.)

You might expect the stress concentration to have a relatively simple effect on the fatigue life, where the new maximum stress value could be found from the unnotched *S–N* curve. But the stress concentration is high at the notch and then decreases away from it; so, a crack, as it initiates and grows away from the notch, experiences a decreasing stress field. The nucleation of a fatigue crack is accelerated in the region of high stress,

and in the region away from the notch the stresses drop to the nominal applied values. The change in stress due to the presence of a stress concentration is illustrated in Figure 2.30.

We can represent the actual fall in fatigue strength by a notch-sensitivity factor q, which clearly depends on both the notch severity and the material:

$$q = \frac{\alpha_f - 1}{\alpha_k - 1} \tag{2.5}$$

where α_f is the fatigue notch factor:

$$\alpha_f = \frac{\text{fatigue strength of unnotched specimen}}{\text{fatigue strength of notched specimen}} \tag{2.6}$$

A high notch sensitivity q means that a notched specimen has a low fatigue strength compared with that of an unnotched sample; a low notch sensitivity means that the notch has not affected the fatigue strength to a great degree. ▷

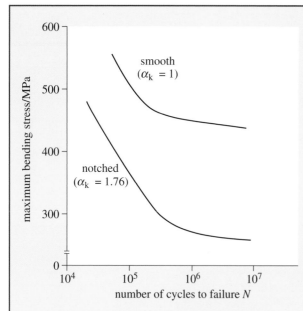

Figure 2.29 *S–N* curves for smooth and notched test-pieces

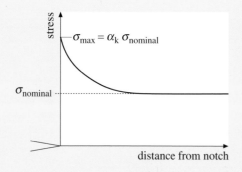

Figure 2.30 Reduction in stress with increased distance from a stress-concentrating notch

At one extreme, a notch may have a greater effect on the fatigue strength than it has on the peak stress from its stress concentrating effect (so $\alpha_f > \alpha_k$ and $q > 1$). At the other extreme, the material would not be sensitive to the presence of notches, i.e. $\alpha_f = 1$ and $q = 0$. The value of q can be anything from zero up to a value in excess of one; however, values are usually between $q = 0$ and $q = 1$.

SAQ 2.2 (Learning outcomes 2.2 and 2.3)

What are the fatigue notch factor α_f and the notch-sensitivity factor q at each value of α_k for the cases given in Table 2.1?

Table 2.1 Reverse axial fatigue limits σ_{FL} for samples of EN 8 steel with various values of α_k

α_k	σ_{FL}/MPa
1	232
1.84	137
2.26	120
3.02	108
4.6	86
7.06	91

Hint: calculate the values of α_f relative to the case of no stress concentration ($\alpha_k = 1$). △

The answer to SAQ 2.2 shows how the value of q is not constant, but is dependent on the stress concentration. Interestingly, you can note that there is a bigger reduction in fatigue life for a relatively small stress concentration. △

2.1.4 Environmental effects

The environment in which a component operates can have a significant effect on its fatigue properties, particularly in high-cycle (low stress amplitude) fatigue. Even air has a deleterious effect, as moisture and oxygen tend to at least cause some oxidation. Typically, moisture in the air lowers the fatigue strength of most metals and alloys by 5–15%.

Environments that are more corrosive than air attack the surface more vigorously, and this results in a significant decrease in fatigue strength. Increasing the temperature accelerates corrosion and oxidation, so this also lowers the fatigue resistance. The term corrosion fatigue is used to describe failure under the combined effects of cyclic loading and a corrosive environment.

2.1.5 Microstructural effects

The fatigue performance of metals and alloys is greatly affected by their microstructure: in particular by the grain size and by the presence of alloying elements.

However, this is not surprising: these factors affect the strength, ductility and toughness of metals, so there is no reason to assume that their fatigue strength also would not be affected. Any microstructural change that strengthens a metal by increasing its yield stress, thereby making plastic deformation more difficult, will improve the fatigue strength of the metal. However, you cannot assume that the fatigue strength is increased by the same proportion as the yield strength; in general, the proportionate increase in the fatigue strength is smaller.

It is often observed that electroplating a component, i.e. depositing a 'clean' metal layer on its surface, leads to a reduction in fatigue strength. Can we explain this phenomenon? Although electroplating provides a relatively smooth protective layer on the surface, if the new surface is soft, then it will readily undergo plastic flow. So the incidence of plastic flow and the resultant damage and crack initiation outweigh the effect of a smooth surface.

In addition, electrodeposits often contain high residual tensile stresses. In the case of hard chromium plate, the electrodeposits may become riddled with microcracks, each of which is a possible fatigue nucleation site.

> ### EXERCISE 2.6
>
> For a given applied stress cycle, the fatigue endurance of a material normally decreases with increasing temperature. Suggest a reason for this effect.

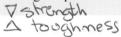

2.2 Strain–life testing

Laboratory tests can also be carried out where the test-piece is subjected to a constant strain amplitude. For plotting the results of a strain cycling test you can consider the stress amplitude in Figure 2.17 to be replaced by strain amplitude, and by analogy with the S–N curve there is a failure curve for strain cycling consisting of the strain amplitude plotted against cycles to failure N. The strains experienced by the test-piece may be completely elastic or a combination of elastic and plastic; and, in relation to fatigue, it is necessary to distinguish between them.

The total strain range $\Delta \varepsilon$ is made up of elastic and plastic strains $\Delta \varepsilon_e$ and $\Delta \varepsilon_p$ respectively:

$$\Delta \varepsilon = \Delta \varepsilon_e + \Delta \varepsilon_p \tag{2.7}$$

By definition, the elastic strain range $\Delta \varepsilon_e$ is related to the stress range $\Delta \sigma$ by Hooke's law:

$$\Delta \varepsilon_e = \frac{\Delta \sigma}{E} \tag{2.8}$$

It follows from Equations (2.7) and (2.8) that the plastic strain range is:

$$\Delta\varepsilon_p = \Delta\varepsilon - \frac{\Delta\sigma}{E}$$

The nucleation and growth of fatigue cracks occurs only when cyclic plastic strains occur, so how is it that cracks initiate at stress levels well below the nominal yield stress? The answer is simply that it is necessary only for plastic strain to occur *locally*; it does not have to occur throughout the section (as it would at the yield stress). In any real component there will always be some stress concentrations due to notches, scratches or microstructural features, and it is here that plastic strain and subsequent fatigue may occur, even though the nominal stress level is below the yield.

When a material is subjected to a constant cyclic strain, it may progressively harden or soften. If it hardens, then the constant strain amplitude is associated with an increasing stress amplitude, referred to as *cyclic hardening*.

Have a look at Figure 2.31, which shows the stress–strain response of a metal deformed cyclically in tension and compression, where there is some plastic deformation. When the metal is deformed from the starting point O to P, it is just like part of a conventional tensile test. Unloading to Q leaves a plastic strain. Loading in compression then causes compressive yielding to S, then unloading to T; the sample does not return to its undeformed state at O when the load is now removed. Loading again in tension will take the sample to R, then the curve will join up again at P, and a *hysteresis loop* is produced.

Figures 2.32(a) and (b) respectively illustrate the behaviour of material that shows cyclic softening and cyclic hardening. Initially, for cyclic softening the peak stress decreases; for cyclic hardening it increases. Eventually, after a sufficient number of cycles, perhaps 1000 or more, the stress amplitude stabilizes at a constant value and a stable or constant hysteresis loop is obtained.

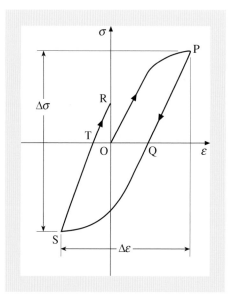

Figure 2.31 Cyclic loading of a metal

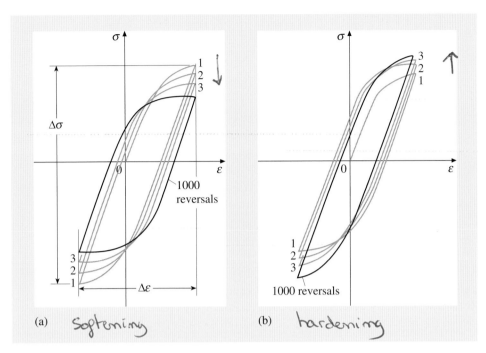

Figure 2.32   (a) Cyclic softening and (b) cyclic hardening

3 USING FATIGUE DATA IN DESIGN

We can conceptually divide the fatigue life of a component into two main stages, i.e. initiation and growth. Although there are a number of specific models that can be used to predict either or both of these phases, and a large number of commercial software packages and finite element programs that claim to make the job easier, there are actually just two fundamental types of predictive fatigue model: safe-life design and damage-tolerant design.

In the *safe-life design* approach, fatigue data are used to calculate how long a component can be used without a critical fatigue crack initiating and growing to the point of component failure. It is assumed implicitly that the majority of the fatigue life is taken up with initiation of the fatigue crack, and that there isn't an identifiable flaw in the component at the start of its life. No analysis is performed on the growth of the crack. However, as mentioned earlier, the definition of precisely when a crack has been initiated is, inevitably, arbitrary. Indeed, in the simplest approaches and tests, a crack is said to have 'initiated' when the specimen fails.

This is the traditional approach to fatigue design. It is particularly well suited to small, highly stressed bodies and it is mathematically simple to use. Thus, the initial 'first pass' design of virtually all components, machines and structures is undertaken using this method. It is also a good way of assessing the inherent fatigue properties of a given material or surface condition.

Conversely, the *damage-tolerant design* approach assumes that a crack always exists at the start of the fatigue life. That is, it assumes that a crack has already initiated and that the fatigue life of the components or structure is dominated and hence controlled by the growth of an initial crack to a size at which failure occurs. When the exact size of the initial crack population is not well known, then an arbitrary, conservative initial crack size is used. The main advantages of this method are that both the kinetics of crack growth and the size when it becomes potentially fatal can be calculated using fracture mechanics. This enables a maintenance schedule to be devised whereby any potentially fatal crack can be identified by inspection well before failure occurs. We will also study this approach later, when you will see that it produces a significant improvement on the structural integrity of safety-critical devices.

Both these fatigue–design philosophies can be incorporated into a so-called *fail-safe design*. If a structure or part of a structure sustains fatigue damage, then there will still be sufficient strength for it to do its job without failing. This can encompass many aspects of a design, including having multiple pathways for load to be transmitted and providing crack stoppers to limit damage to small sections. Fail-safe design, however, did not prevent one of the major fatigue-related accidents in civil aviation, when a transport plane crashed on approach to ☒ **Lusaka** ☒.

3.1 Stress lifing: designing for infinite life

We have seen how the analysis of data from *S–N* curves is relatively straightforward. If we know the cyclic stress *S–N* profile in the material, and we can design our component so that the cyclic stress is below the fatigue limit (or a high-cycle endurance limit), then it will not fail by fatigue.

The use of this approach is really designing a component to have an infinite life (at least from a fatigue point of view, and ignoring other mechanisms such as wear and corrosion). It requires the design stresses to be less than the fatigue limit of the material. Of course, if the material has no fatigue limit this approach cannot be used without caution; knowing the endurance limit at 10^7 cycles is no use for a component that may experience 10^8 or 10^9 cycles during its operating life.

Alternatively, if under a particular design loading it is calculated that a component will fail by fatigue after, say, 20 000 cycles, then instigating a replacement scheme where the component is always replaced after 10 000 cycles will ensure safety. Petrol-driven cars that use polymer-based timing belts require that they be changed regularly, typically after 30 000–60 000 miles running. The belts will fail eventually if not replaced. I know: it happened to me and the consequences were expensive.

As a general approximation, fatigue limits and endurance limits (at 10^8 cycles) are about half the ultimate tensile strength (UTS) of the material. The ratios of fatigue strength to UTS for a few of these materials are shown in Table 2.2.

Table 2.2   Ratios of fatigue limit to ultimate tensile strength for various materials

Material	Fatigue or endurance limit at 10^8 cycles / Ultimate tensile strength
Cast carbon steels	0.4–0.45
Wrought carbon steels	0.4–0.6
Wrought alloy steels	0.4–0.55
Cast aluminium alloys	0.25–0.35
Wrought aluminium alloys	0.35–0.4
Wrought titanium alloys	0.4–0.55

It is also possible to predict how the fatigue life will vary as the mean stress is altered by using the ☑ **Goodman diagram** ☑.

Of course, many cyclic loadings are not of regular repeating amplitudes and constant mean stress, and the loading is often random. So how is the random nature taken into account during the design process? The answer lies in assessing the damage contribution of each cycle and then linearly summing the damage associated with each cycle by using ☑ **Miner's rule** ☑.

☑ Lusaka

On 14 May 1977 a Boeing 707 transport plane crashed on approach to Lusaka airport, in Zambia, when the right horizontal stabilizer (the small 'wing' part of the tailplane assembly) broke away as the result of the failure of its main spar. The aircraft crashed, killing its six crew.

The aircraft had been designed using a fail-safe approach, which was defined as:

> It shall be shown by analysis and/or tests that catastrophic failure or excessive deformation, which could adversely affect the flight characteristics of the aeroplane, are not probable after fatigue failure or obvious partial failure of a single principal structural element. After such failure, the remaining structure shall be capable of withstanding static loads corresponding with the flight loading condition specified.
>
> Civil Aeronautics Board (1956)

The airframe had been certified as meeting these requirements.

However, the actual behaviour of the structure when there was failure of the critical spar was not as predicted. The design of the spar (Figure 2.33) was effectively an I-beam. The design included a central stiffening bar, at the middle of the web, to act as a crack stopper in the case that the upper flange failed. That was exactly what happened, but the redistribution of load as a result of the failure meant that the crack simply kept going all the way through the entire spar.

The design, therefore, was not fail-safe as its designers had envisaged. Additionally, in this case there had been changes to the stabilizer design that had not been fatigue tested.

A critical conclusion of the accident report was that use of damage-tolerant design, with inspection, could have prevented the accident. This effectively marked the end of the use of fail-safe design in civil aviation, and a move to damage-tolerant design with inspection.

Figure 2.33 The failed component in the Lusaka crash: (a) a picture of the horizontal stabilizer of the type that failed; (b) internal structure of the stabilizer; (c) the fractured component showing the failed, 'fail-safe' chord, plus (d) a schematic of the web cross section at the failure point

☑ Goodman diagram

The *Goodman diagram* is a plot of stress amplitude σ_a against mean stress σ_m, as shown in Figure 2.34(a). The limits of the plot are the maximum possible mean stress on the *x*-axis (i.e. the tensile strength of the material σ_t) and σ_{a0} on the *y*-axis, where σ_{a0} is the fatigue limit when the mean stress is zero (i.e. an alternating stress as in Figure 2.17a). In materials that do not have a fatigue limit this would be the endurance limit. The fatigue and endurance limits under zero mean stress can conveniently be determined from rotating bend tests.

For a material with a fatigue limit to have an infinite life under cyclic loading, the point corresponding to the values of the mean stress and the stress amplitude for the particular case must lie below the straight line on the Goodman diagram. Since this graph is linear, combinations of stress amplitude σ_a and mean stress σ_m that lie on this line (e.g. the point marked on Figure 2.34a) can be expressed by:

$$\sigma_a = \sigma_{a0}\left(1 - \frac{\sigma_m}{\sigma_t}\right) \qquad (2.9)$$

As the Goodman line effectively describes how the fatigue limit varies with mean stress, it draws a boundary between values of σ_a and σ_m that are 'safe' and the values that will eventually lead to fatigue failure. There are various modifications that can be made to Equation (2.9), and the exact shape of the line, but this is a useful first approximation.

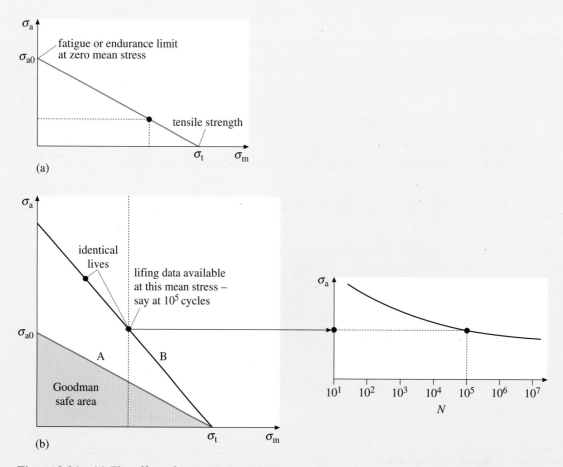

Figure 2.34   (a) The effect of mean stress on fatigue strength; (b) using the Goodman construction to calculate fatigue life

Where the Goodman diagram becomes useful is for assessing what happens to a component subjected to fatigue cycles of different mean stresses and stress amplitudes, where fatigue data have been measured at one mean stress only. Have a look at Figure 2.34(b), showing a Goodman plot and an associated S–N curve. The line labelled A is the Goodman line showing the variation of the fatigue limit. The upper line, labelled B, is constructed by taking the point where the S–N curve gives a life of 10^5 cycles and drawing a line down to the tensile strength, which is a known material limit. This line then tells us what values of stress amplitude and mean stress will give the same lifetime.

EXERCISE 2.7

A sample of a titanium alloy is found to have a fatigue limit of 200 MPa when tested with a mean stress of zero. What would be the material's likely fatigue limit when exposed to a mean stress in service of 100 MPa if it has a tensile stress of 500 MPa?

SAQ 2.3 (Learning outcomes 2.2 and 2.4)

An aluminium alloy with a tensile stress of 420 MPa is known to have an endurance limit of 120 MPa when exposed to a mean stress of 200 MPa. What is its likely endurance limit at a mean stress of zero, using the Goodman relation?

☑ Miner's rule

Miner's rule is a numerical method that is used to solve the problem of estimating the life under complex service conditions. Such conditions are quite likely to involve cycles of varying amplitude such as those shown in Figure 2.17(e). Methods exist for counting the cycles within such a complicated spectrum (for example, the so-called 'rainflow' method). To illustrate the problem Figure 2.35(a) shows the load history experienced by a suspension component on a vehicle driven round a test circuit. The resulting load spectrum of this range of data will consist of a number of load cycles of specified amplitude and mean value.

Figure 2.35(b) shows a sample of a complex stress variation, where there are three regions with different stress amplitudes, frequencies, and numbers of cycles. Miner's rule relates each of these to the S–N curve; it is the simplest and oldest empirical law with which to predict (from S–N curves) the fatigue life under varying stresses.

Miner's rule takes each stress amplitude, uses the S–N curve to find the total life at that value (Figure 2.35c) and then assesses how much of the life has been 'used up' by the actual number of stress cycles applied at each amplitude.

Suppose that a specimen undergoes n_1 stress cycles at a stress amplitude σ_{a1} and a mean stress σ_m, and that the expected life under these conditions according to the S–N curve is N_1. The ratio n_1/N_1 is then taken as a measure of the fatigue life that has been 'used up' at that stress amplitude.

Miner's law assumes that failure occurs when the sum of the ratios for all the stress amplitudes involved equals unity. The rule implies that there is a linear accumulation of damage during fatigue and that fracture will occur when:

$$\frac{n_1}{N_1} + \frac{n_2}{N_2} + \frac{n_3}{N_3} + \ldots + \frac{n_i}{N_i} = 1$$

That is:

$$\sum_i \frac{n_i}{N_i} = 1 \qquad (2.10)$$

The major limitation of the law is that it ignores the possible effects of any prior stress history that the component may have experienced.

For example, it is well known that overstressing increases the fatigue life during subsequent cyclic loading. Overloading an existing crack causes plastic blunting of the crack tip, which temporarily slows, or even halts, its growth. One of the crucial factors in the Comet airliner

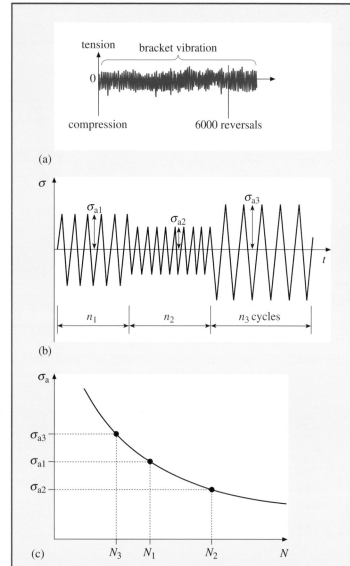

(a)

(b)

(c)

Figure 2.35 (a) The recorded load history of a vehicle suspension component; (b) schematic of different stress cycles within a complex loading pattern; (c) relation of the different stresses to the *S–N* curve

disasters was exactly that; although the aircraft had undergone simulation fatigue testing, the fuselage used for this testing had also previously been used for an overpressure proof test of the structure. This had caused localized blunting by plasticity at the window corners, i.e. the stress concentrators that initiated the failures; as a result, the fatigue life of the test fuselage was considerably longer than that of the planes released into service.

Miner's rule takes no account of such effects. Therefore, it is not surprising that, in practice, failure after loading at variable stress amplitude does not always occur according to Equation (2.10). In a number of cases when the values of this equation at failure were established, it was found that it did not equate to unity, but can lie both above and below unity, depending upon the sequence of load cycles, the magnitude of the mean stress and the type of material. To take account of this a safety factor has been incorporated, so that the rule states that at failure:

$$\sum_i \frac{n_i}{N_i} = C \qquad (2.11)$$

where 0.3–0.8 would be a typical range for C. Although more effective cumulative damage laws are available, Miner's rule offers a simplified approach for some situations. More modern techniques are based on strain amplitude methods, or using the peak stress experienced in each cycle as a 'damage parameter' to apply a correction to measured data.

3.2 Strain lifing: designing for a finite life

Many components cannot be designed in such a way that the stress within them can be reduced to the point where their fatigue life will be effectively infinite. A challenge for many designers, then, is to assess what the life of a component is likely to be.

You already know that finite element analysis is now ubiquitous in the analysis of structural components. Finite element analysis in itself cannot provide fatigue predictions: elements cannot be assigned fatigue properties in the same way as mechanical properties. Instead, what finite element models can do is to identify regions of a structure where there are high strain amplitudes from which the designer can extrapolate the fatigue life from known data on the material.

Up to this point all our design criteria have been in terms of stress level. So what happens in the low-cycle fatigue regime where plastic strain is predominant, and where the properties are best described using plastic strain amplitude rather than stress amplitude? In this regime the amount of plasticity can be sufficient to cause failure in a very low number of cycles, and in extreme cases one cycle may be sufficient. Some useful empirical relations have been developed, based on the results of extensive testing programmes in which a strain amplitude is imposed on the specimen.

For example, the empirical relation between the cyclic elastic strain range $\Delta\varepsilon_e$ and the number of cycles to failure is found to have the form:

$$\Delta\varepsilon_e = 3.5\left(\frac{\sigma_t}{E}\right)N^{-0.12} \tag{2.12}$$

where σ_t is the tensile strength, E is Young's modulus and N is the number of strain cycles to cause fatigue failure. However, as I have already suggested, it is now well established that, in the low-cycle regime, fatigue lifetime is controlled primarily by the magnitude of the range of *plastic* strain in the material. This plastic component of strain forms the basis of the *Manson–Coffin relation* and is best described by:

$$\Delta\varepsilon_p = N^{-0.6}\varepsilon_f^{0.6} \tag{2.13}$$

where $\Delta\varepsilon_p$ is the cyclic plastic strain range, N is the number of cycles to failure and ε_f is the value of true strain at which fracture occurs in a tensile test.

Equations (2.12) and (2.13) were both determined from an analysis of 29 different materials. However, there was a considerable amount of scatter between the experimental data points and the lines describing the equations. This is why the designer needs to be very conservative in using such equations in predictions!

To model both elastic and plastic components, Equations (2.12) and (2.13) can be added together to give N as a function of the total cyclic strain range:

$$\Delta\varepsilon = \Delta\varepsilon_e + \Delta\varepsilon_p = 3.5\left(\frac{\sigma_t}{E}\right)N^{-0.12} + N^{-0.6}\varepsilon_f^{0.6} \tag{2.14}$$

As Figure 2.36 shows, this combined equation produces a curved graph (plotted on logarithmic scales) of strain amplitude against cycles-to-failure that matches the straight elastic and plastic lines with reasonable fit. In this graph it can be seen that, as might be expected, the total strain curve approaches the plastic strain–life curve at large strain amplitudes and approaches the elastic strain line at low strain amplitudes.

The result of testing this predictive equation against axial fatigue data for a number of low- and high-strength steels is shown in Figure 2.37. You can see that the fit between theory and experiment is good, where the points on the graph are actual data from testing and the solid line has been derived from Equation (2.14).

So, using these empirical equations produces accurate predictions, provided that the material is experiencing similar conditions to those of the tested specimens from which the data were originally derived. Predicting finite life using these techniques

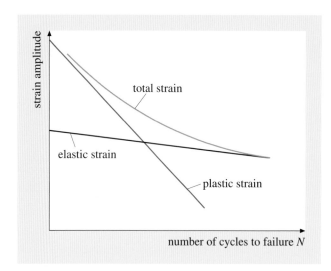

Figure 2.36 A graph of total strain amplitude versus strain cycles to failure, showing the elastic and plastic components of strain

is often referred to as the 'local stress–strain approach'. This procedure relies on accurate modelling of the elastic–plastic stresses and strains at stress concentrators; so, if finite element data are used as the starting point for fatigue analysis of this type, the accuracy of the results is all important.

This has been only the briefest review of empirical methods for estimating the fatigue life. Its purpose has been simply to give you a general impression of what can be done with the results of laboratory tests.

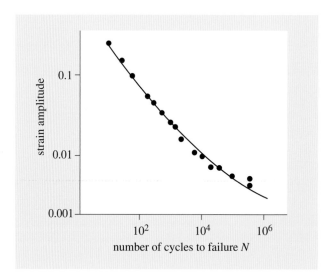

Figure 2.37 Comparison of predicted and experimental fatigue life under strain cycling for various low-alloy and high-strength steels

4 APPLYING FRACTURE MECHANICS TO FATIGUE

At the start of this part, I indicated that the fatigue life of a component can be divided into two stages: the time for a crack to initiate and the time for a crack to grow to a critical length.

When components contain pre-existing flaws, or design features that result in high stress concentrations, the crack-initiation portion of the fatigue life of a component may be significantly reduced to the point where it can effectively be ignored, and it is assumed that a crack will start to grow from the first cycle. As a result, the useful life of these components may be governed by the rate of subcritical crack growth.

In ☑ **the aircraft industry** ☑, for example, designs cannot be overly conservative, simply because the aeroplane would be so heavy that it wouldn't be able to take off! So this leads to highly stressed parts that are susceptible to fatigue. This is well understood in aircraft design, so is not a problem. The fatigue mechanisms are well characterized. Of course, a factor of safety is still used to ensure that the design parameters are relatively conservative, while still allowing the plane to get airborne.

You have seen in the previous sections that in some components the crack-propagation life is neglected during design because strain levels are high, whereas for other components the crack-growth life forms a substantial portion of the total life of the component. For these cases, designing for either an infinite or a finite life can be implemented. Unfortunately, the methods are not totally foolproof, as the Comet case study earlier illustrated, and as does ☑ **the F-111 story** ☑.

☑ The aircraft industry

Between the Comet crashes and the Lusaka accident aircraft designers could choose between safe-life approach and fail-safe approaches for their airframe structures. Fail-safe was pretty well universally adopted by commercial aircraft designers. It was very attractive, because the redundant load paths, such as the central stringer chord in the Lusaka 'beam', meant less concern about the details of fatigue crack-growth rates and a more comfortable operating environment. Military folk would not countenance aircraft carrying redundant weight that would affect performance, and were less influenced by cost considerations, so they chose a safe-life approach. Fail-safe, as an airframe design philosophy effectively came to an abrupt halt in 1978, after the Lusaka accident showed that it was severely flawed.

The solution is the methodology known as damage-tolerant design: here, components and structures are made to tolerate limited structural damage in the form of cracking, with inspection carried out on a regular basis to ensure that any damage is within specified limits. Damage tolerance relies on having some element of redundancy in the structure, but it is fundamentally different from the fail-safe approach.

Damage-tolerance prediction relies on the application of linear elastic fracture mechanics (LEFM), which, with some careful manipulation, contributes enormously to the understanding of the behaviour of cracks when subjected to cyclic loading. By knowing the crack-growth rates in any particular material, designers can time inspection and maintenance schedules. This means that, by inspecting at regular intervals, any cracks that do propagate in a component will not have sufficient time to grow to a size sufficiently long to cause catastrophic failure.

▷

In damage-tolerance prediction, crack initiation is not considered significant and the largest proportion of the fatigue life is used up in propagating the crack. So, by applying fracture mechanics to the problem, it is possible to predict accurately the number of cycles it will take to grow the crack to a specific length. Figure 2.38 illustrates schematically how this process works, from the first detectable crack to the predicted length at which the component should be replaced or repaired.

Nowadays the issue is whether damage tolerance is practical or not – effectively, can the part be inspected? If damage tolerance is not practical, then safe-life is the way to go; if it is practical, then our predictive capability for fatigue-crack growth combined with experiment and in-service experience means that damage-tolerance principles are universally used.

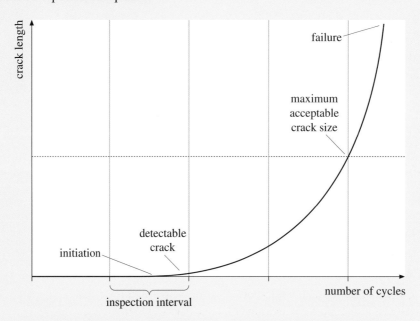

Figure 2.38   Damage-tolerant design, using inspection to detect and monitor growing cracks

☑ The F-111 story

The F-111, shown in Figure 2.39, was one of the first aircraft designed for safe life. However, following several early aircraft losses, it became clear that relatively small flaws not detected during inspection after manufacture could lead to catastrophic failure in the highly stressed, high-strength steel structure, following rapid fatigue-crack growth. One example was the loss of a wing from one aircraft while on a training flight. During a high-stress 'pull-up' manoeuvre, catastrophic failure occurred in the wing-pivot assembly.

The failure was found to have initiated from a forging lap (where the forged material had not flowed evenly into its required form), which was not detected at the manufacturing stage, and from which a crack grew to failure in only 100 flight hours. The safe-life design of the aircraft had predicted a life 100 times longer than this would be achieved, and that included a safety factor of 4. The safe-life approach does not take into account that the high-strength steel used in critical, highly stressed parts of the structure has relatively low toughness and can, therefore, fracture under load in the presence of relatively small defects. Unforeseen, small flaws can, therefore, negate the safe-life design calculations that were used.

Clearly, simply selecting a new safe life of 100 flight hours based on experience was not an option. A new approach was needed.

Since the F-111 was already designed and built, little could be done to change the materials or stresses. The solution to ensuring the integrity of the airframe was a low-temperature proof test, with each airframe individually tested before being passed as safe for service.

The proof test was designed using fracture mechanics principles: the low temperature reduced the toughness of the steel components used, so ensuring a safety factor at operating temperatures; the loads applied would cause an existing defect to propagate to failure if one existed. If the airframe passed the test, then any defects must be below a certain size, and damage-tolerance calculations, based on the rate of growth of such defects if they did exist, could ensure the structure's safety up to the next scheduled test.

Figure 2.39 An F-111 with its wings still attached

4.1 The application of linear-elastic fracture mechanics to fatigue

Fracture mechanics is the mechanics of *cracked* bodies, so it follows that it can be applied only to cases where crack initiation has already occurred. In other words, fracture mechanics can be applied only to crack *growth*. In this approach, we are concerned with propagation of the fatigue crack over distances that are large in comparison with the scale of the atomic structure, i.e. when the crack is in Stage II of its development.

Structural maintenance in the aircraft industry is dictated by the serious economic consequences of major damage or loss of the aircraft, compared with the cost of an inspection programme required to find early damage. Fracture mechanics is vital for the maintenance of aging aircraft, using damage-tolerance principles, by combining inspection with the ability to predict fatigue crack-growth rates based on LEFM principles. The opportunity and ease of inspection is integrated with analysis to ensure that damage is likely to be detected before aeroplane safety is jeopardized. What LEFM brings is the ability to predict the growth rate of long cracks, which is vital to the aircraft industry.

A fatigue crack that grows under cyclic loading is small for most of its life; this is the stage of initiation occurring before we would consider it to be 'detectable'. Once the crack has become 'long' its progress and direction are controlled by the opening stress. Also, the crack's growth rate is also largely independent of the metal's microstructure – metallic microstructures tend to be of the scale of tens of micrometres (a typical grain size), whereas a 'long' crack will be of the order of a few millimetres.

In Part 1 you saw that LEFM can predict whether a crack in a structure will cause brittle fracture. With hindsight, the application of LEFM to fatigue seems to be an obvious extension of the ideas coming from brittle-fracture research. This is because a fatigue crack growing slowly and stably in the body of a metal component has only a small plastic zone surrounded by bulk elastic material. Historically, there has been a lot of resistance to the notion that an elastic parameter could describe an event that is driven by the small plastic events at the crack tip.

The idea is simple: if the cyclic stress range or amplitude is driving a fatigue crack, and stress is related to the stress-intensity factor K and crack length a, then there ought to be a relationship between the stress-intensity factor range ΔK and the change in crack length, i.e. the crack-growth rate.

From Part 1, we know that for static loading the stress-intensity factor K is given by:

$$K = Y\sigma\sqrt{\pi a} \tag{2.15}$$

where Y is a dimensionless factor depending on the geometry, σ is the nominal tensile stress and a is the crack length (for a surface crack) or the half-length (for an internal crack).

In cyclic loading, K varies over the stress-intensity range ΔK, where:

$$\begin{aligned}
\Delta K &= K_{max} - K_{min} \\
&= Y\left(\sigma_{max} - \sigma_{min}\right)\sqrt{\pi a} \\
&= Y\Delta\sigma\sqrt{\pi a}
\end{aligned} \tag{2.16}$$

The experimental data supporting this theory are compelling, as shown in Figure 2.40. For a specific metal species it doesn't matter much what the alloy is, or what the heat treatment was; the data for a wide range of values of ΔK fall on a line described by:

$$\frac{\mathrm{d}a}{\mathrm{d}N} = C\left(\Delta K\right)^m \tag{2.17}$$

where $\mathrm{d}a/\mathrm{d}N$ is the crack-growth rate, and C and m are material constants. Equation (2.17) is known as the Paris equation. It applies to Region 2 in the centre portion of the graph in Figure 2.40. The Paris equation isn't universally applicable to all fatigue-crack-growth behaviour, though.

- Region 1 is where ΔK is low: the crack is short and its growth is microstructure and load dominated. Only when cracks are larger than the scale of the microstructure by a factor of typically 4–5 does the Paris equation hold true.

- The lower limit of ΔK is called the threshold for crack growth, ΔK_{th}. When the range of stress-intensity factor in a cracked component is less than ΔK_{th}, the crack will not propagate under the existing conditions of, for example, stress and temperature. Clearly, ΔK_{th} has some significance as a possible design criterion for fatigue conditions in components that already contain cracks, such as welded joints. The actual value of ΔK_{th} is very sensitive to mean stress and environment, but a reasonable figure for a typical steel is around 6 MPa $\sqrt{m}$.

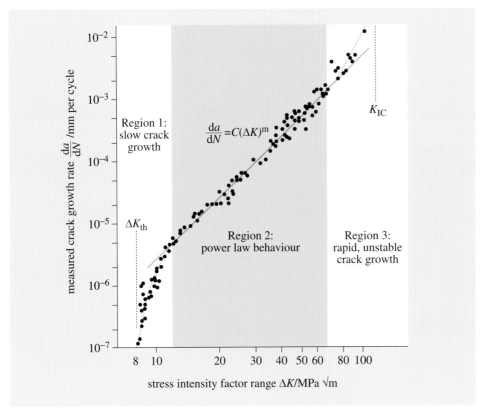

Figure 2.40 Fatigue crack growth

- In Region 3, where K exceeds about $0.7K_{IC}$ and approaches the material's fracture toughness, the growth rate accelerates due to load-controlled 'static' crack-growth mechanisms.

Data such as those in Figure 2.40 have to be obtained by rather more complex testing than generating S–N fatigue data, as described in ☑ **Measuring crack-growth rates** ☑.

☑ Measuring crack-growth rates

Stress–life and strain–life fatigue tests, used to construct an S–N or ε–N curve, are relatively straightforward. Each sample is placed in a test machine, the appropriate cyclic stress or strain amplitude is selected, the operator goes off to do something else and the machine counts the number of cycles until the sample fails.

The measurement of crack-growth rates is more complex, simply because the crack has to be monitored continuously as the applied load is

cycled. This is not only so that the change in crack length over a given number of cycles can be measured, but also because the crack length is needed to calculate the values of K that the crack tip experiences as a result of the applied loading.

One highly tedious method is to apply, say, 1000 load cycles and then measure the crack extension using a microscope with an accurate measuring gauge; but such methods are used only rarely today. Another method is to bond

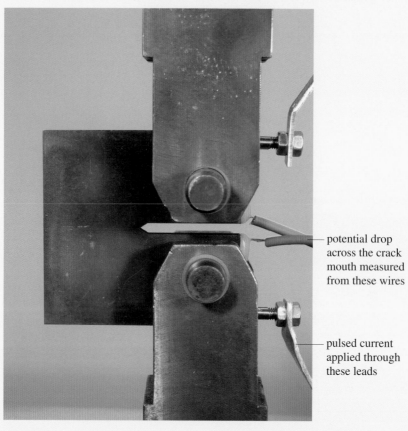

potential drop
across the crack
mouth measured
from these wires

pulsed current
applied through
these leads

Figure 2.41   Experimental set-up for monitoring crack length by the potential-drop method

an array of wires, similar to a strain gauge, to the surface of the test-piece and note the number of cycles as the crack successively cuts each wire.

Most common, though, are so-called 'potential-drop' techniques, where a high electrical current is passed through the sample and the potential drop, i.e. the voltage, is measured across the crack. The potential drop will only be small, given the very low electrical resistance of the metal specimens used, but it is detectable and can be monitored accurately using modern electronics. Figure 2.41 shows a typical experimental set-up.

As the crack grows, there is an increase in the sample's electrical resistance, because the conduction area is smaller. The potential drop across the crack increases.

For a particular sample geometry this effect can be calibrated, allowing continuous monitoring of the crack length. This then allows automation of crack-growth tests, as the data can be logged automatically, and computer control can be used to adjust the loads during the test to maintain a particular value of ΔK, for example.

Throughout the 1960s there was little industrial interest in Paris's work until the major F-111 failure I've already described. The wing was lost when the forging flaw extended only about 10% of its original length due to fatigue. The fleet was grounded for 6 months. Solving the F-111 problem, which was politically and commercially so important, moved fracture mechanics into the vanguard of engineering techniques. And, as I mentioned previously, this accident also introduced the notion of damage tolerance into the military aircraft industry. Certainly, damage tolerance is not possible without the ability to calculate crack-growth rates, and, uniquely, this is what the Paris equation provides.

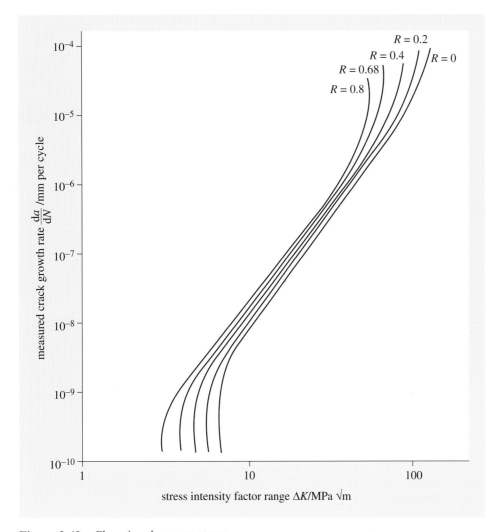

Figure 2.42   Changing the mean stress

Since the 1960s the data confirming the Paris relationship have become overwhelming. The final, compelling piece of experimental evidence in favour of the Paris relationship is shown in Figure 2.42. This shows that varying the mean stress, and therefore R, has only a minimal effect in Region 2 on the Paris results; there is an increase in crack-growth rates as the mean stress increases (we shall see why shortly), but the overall profile is unchanged.

4.2 Using the Paris law

For the Paris relationship (Equation (2.17), the coefficient C and exponent m are, unfortunately, unit dependent: they will be different depending on whether the applied stress is expressed in pascals or pounds per square inch (psi) and on whether the crack is measured in metres or inches. Some branches of engineering, notably those based and supplying to the US markets, still work in imperial units.

For units of metres and megapascals, some common values are shown in Table 2.3.

Table 2.3   Common values of C and m for metals

Material	C	m
Steel	10^{-11}	3
Aluminium	10^{-12}	3
Nickel	4×10^{-12}	3.3
Titanium	10^{-11}	5

Combining the LEFM equation (Equation 2.15) and the Paris equation (Equation 2.17) produces:

$$\frac{da}{dN} = C\left(\Delta K\right)^{m} = C\left(Y\Delta\sigma\sqrt{\pi a}\right)^{m}$$

This equation, after rearranging for dN, can be integrated directly provided that Y is constant:

$$dN = \frac{da}{C\left(\Delta K\right)^{m}} = \frac{da}{C\left(Y\Delta\sigma\sqrt{\pi a}\right)^{m}}$$

$$\int_{0}^{N_{f}} dN = \int_{a_{i}}^{a_{f}} \frac{da}{C\left(Y\Delta\sigma\sqrt{\pi a}\right)^{m}}$$

where a_i and a_f are the initial and final crack lengths respectively and N_f is the number of cycles to failure.

If Y is not a function of a:

$$N_f = \frac{1}{C\left(Y\Delta\sigma\sqrt{\pi}\right)^{m}} \int_{a_i}^{a_f} a^{-m/2} \, da$$

So:

$$N_f = \frac{1}{C\left(Y\Delta\sigma\sqrt{\pi}\right)^{m}} \frac{1}{1 - \frac{m}{2}} \left[a_f^{1-(m/2)} - a_i^{1-(m/2)} \right] \tag{2.18}$$

Substituting a typical value of m into the equation (here I am using $m = 4$, which is common for many steels) and making use of Equation (2.3) gives the result:

$$N_f = \frac{1}{C\left(Y2\sigma_a\right)^{4} \pi^2 a_i} \left(1 - \frac{a_i}{a_f}\right) \tag{2.19}$$

Obviously this is a very useful expression, for if we know the initial and final crack lengths, the stress range, and the material's fatigue properties, then we can calculate the number of cycles needed to propagate the crack to any given length.

SAQ 2.4 (Learning outcomes 2.2 and 2.6)

How many cycles would it take to grow a crack from 4 mm to 8 mm in a component that is subjected to a stress range of 80 MPa, in a geometry where Y is a constant 1.2, and the material properties in the Paris equation are $m = 4$ and $C = 10^{-11}$, where $\Delta\sigma$ is in MPa?

Numerical integration is usually required if Y is dependent on a, i.e. Y is not constant.

This approach uses the applied stress range to calculate crack growth, and we will explore this further in the next section. K is then derived from the geometry of the situation via Y. It does assume that there is a direct link between σ_{max} and K_{max}, and between σ_{min} and K_{min}. This is what fracture mechanics tells us is the case, but situations can arise where what happens at K_{min} becomes complicated, as when ☑ **crack closure** ☑ occurs.

☑ Crack closure

The use of the Paris equation to predict successfully the propagation rate of a fatigue crack relies on the assumption that the stress-intensity range ΔK is a true measure of the *crack-driving force* that the crack tip experiences during cyclic loading, which leads to crack advance. So the crack-growth rate does not depend on the absolute values of K_{max} and K_{min}, but only on the difference between them. An obvious exception is when K_{max} approaches or exceeds the fracture toughness K_{IC} of the material. In this case, static, not fatigue, failure is expected. Also, stress-intensity factors cannot take negative values, since the compressive loads are carried by the crack faces, which prevent the crack tip from experiencing any 'opening' loads. Therefore, K_{min} is taken as zero for cyclic loading at negative stress ratios ($R < 0$) on the assumption that the crack will 'close up' at zero load.

However, laboratory tests show that the crack propagation rate does also depend on stress ratio R; this is exemplified by Figure 2.42: increasing the mean stress (which means increasing R) does cause acceleration of the crack-growth rate.

This effect is a result of the permanent plastic deformation that occurs as the crack tip is loaded during each cycle. This leaves a plastic 'wake' behind the growing crack (Figure 2.43), within which contact between the crack faces can occur even during the tensile portion of the fatigue cycle. The crack faces near the crack tip will require a somewhat larger applied tensile stress to 'open up'. Effectively this means that the crack can be 'closed' during part of the stress cycling, when the nominal K is above K_{min}; hence the term 'crack closure'.

The consequence of crack closure is to decrease the actual stress-intensity range that the crack tip experiences from its nominal (applied) value of ΔK to an effective (lesser) value of ΔK_{eff}, defined as $\Delta K_{eff} = K_{max} - K_{cl}$, where K_{cl} is the stress-intensity factor at which the two fracture surfaces first come into contact during the unloading portion of the stress cycle (Figure 2.44).

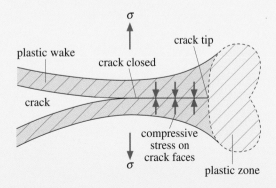

Figure 2.43 Premature closure of crack tip due to plastic deformation in the wake of the crack

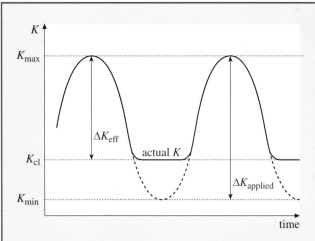

Figure 2.44   Schematic illustration of crack closure

The use of ΔK_{eff} instead of ΔK in the Paris equation enables the crack-growth rates shown in Figure 2.45(a), obtained at different stress ratios, to collapse into a single line as seen in Figure 2.45(b).

K_{cl} is difficult, if not impossible, to determine by analytical modelling methods. Therefore, various experimental methods have been developed for its measurement. The simplest and most reliable ones rely on the measurement of the specimen's compliance by strategically positioned strain gauges around the crack tip. The level at which the crack closes (or opens, depending on whether loading up or down) can be determined by the deviation of the strain gauge reading from linearity (Figure 2.46).

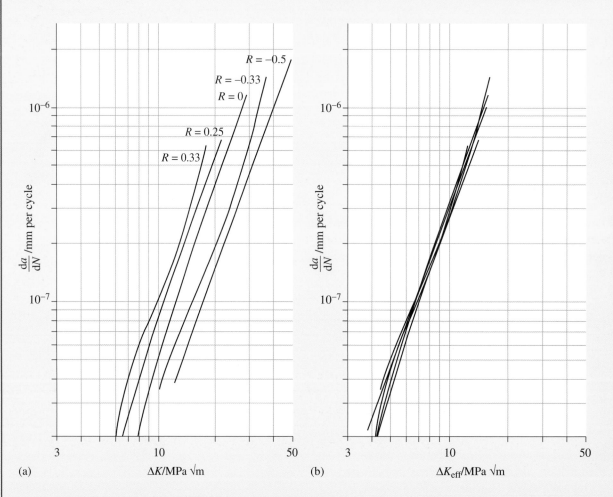

Figure 2.45   Using ΔK_{eff} to analyse fatigue crack-growth data: (a) influence of R on fatigue crack growth; (b) crack-growth rate data correlated by ΔK_{eff}

Besides *plasticity-induced* crack closure, there are other mechanisms that can contribute. Two of the most important of these are shown schematically in Figure 2.47, where it is illustrated that oxide deposits formed on the freshly created crack surfaces (Figure 2.47a), and asperities on uneven crack surfaces (Figure 2.47b), can cause premature crack closure.

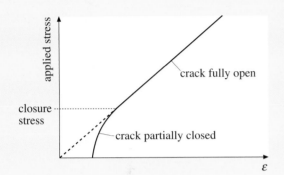

Figure 2.46   Measurement of crack closure from strain data

Figure 2.47   Schematic description of other crack-closure mechanisms: (a) corrosion debris; (b) roughness induced (adapted from Suresh, S. and Ritchie, R. O., 1982)

4.3 Practical fatigue analysis

No one carries out manual integration any more – that is what computers are for. Here, I shall use the 'Fatigue calculator' spreadsheet to show the use of the Paris equation.

Open the Fatigue calculator. As for the K calculator, there are purple boxes for entering properties and a drop-down menu for choosing the geometry of interest. If they are not there already, put 10^{-11} and 3, the values for C and m for steel, into the 'Material properties' boxes.

Now put 3 mm and 4 mm for initial crack length and final crack length, for an edge-cracked plate in tension, and 16 mm for width W into the geometry boxes. Put a stress range of 100 MPa into the loading box and an increment of 0.5 mm into the increment box.

When you hit the calculate box, what will happen is that the Paris equation will be solved numerically for two increments of crack growth: from 3 mm to 3.5 mm and 3.5 mm to 4 mm. You should find that the calculator produces an answer of 27 693 cycles (Figure 2.48). So for this geometry, in this material, with this stress range, the spreadsheet tells us a crack will grow from 3 mm to 4 mm length in 27 693 load cycles.

EXERCISE 2.8

Is this increment of 0.5 mm acceptable, or a bit coarse? Use smaller increments to see the effect of changing this parameter. Note down the number of cycles to grow the crack for 0.05, 0.005 and 0.0005 and 0.00005 mm.

Figure 2.48   Screen dump of the 'Fatigue' interface for an edge-cracked plate in tension, showing 27 693 cycles to failure

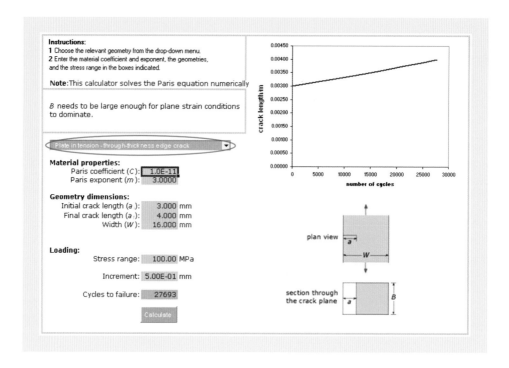

The exercise shows that the increment size is important. This is because the crack accelerates as it grows, i.e. as Y increases. So taking an average over 0.5 mm is not sensible, because in reality the value of Y would have risen sufficiently over that distance to increase the values of K and so ΔK. The calculator shows this: the curving graph of crack length against cycles with the growth rate (the slope of the graph) increases as the crack gets longer (Figure 2.49). Exercise 2.9 also illustrates this.

Figure 2.49   Plate in tension with a through-thickness edge crack: the slope of the graph increases as the crack grows from 3 mm to 8 mm

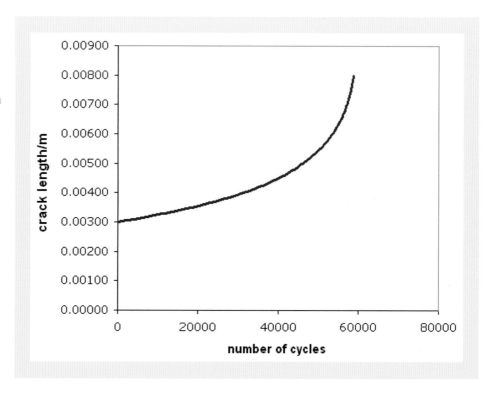

EXERCISE 2.9

Set up your calculator for 1000 (0.0005 mm) increments. How many cycles does it take for the crack to grow from 3 mm to 3.2 mm and how many to grow from 3.8 mm to 4 mm?

The answer to the exercise shows that growing the crack the first 0.2 mm takes something like twice as long as the last 0.2 mm. This is in the nature of fatigue cracks: they spend most of their life being young and accelerate to failure during the latter stages of their life – I know the feeling.

I am now going to return to the pressure-vessel design problem from Section 3.1 of Part 1. I'll make life a bit easier by assuming that we now have a steel supplier who can guarantee that our grade of steel stays on the upper shelf at 0 °C and we have increased the wall thickness of the design to 18 mm. We have also specified pre- and post-weld heat treatment and agreed a fabrication specification that includes 100% inspection for surface flaws – this is an expensive piece of kit we're designing – which guarantees finding any cracks over 3 mm. So the current design parameters are as follows:

- The fracture toughness of the material is a fixed 140 MPa √m.

- Also fixed are the residual stresses, at 100 MPa, the design stresses, at 300 MPa, and the thermal shock stresses, at 150 MPa; the first two are in tension and the third is in bending.

- The wall thickness has increased to 18 mm.

- The length of an unfound crack is 3 mm.

SAQ 2.5 (Block 2 Part 1 revision)

We need to recalculate the K values for the pressure-vessel example in order to produce the new reserve factor on load. Use the K calculator spreadsheet now to do this.

Hint: remember that you have to work out the individual K values from each source, and sum them.

You now have to recommend an inspection cycle for the operation of the plant, to account for the growth, by fatigue, of any pre-existing flaws. The non-destructive evaluation firm will 'guarantee' to find cracks over 3 mm. On start-up there is a surge, and so the plant suffers a one-off cyclic stress excursion of ±50 MPa and start-up happens, on average, 10 times a day. This surge increases the design loading of the plant.

SAQ 2.6 (Block 2 Part 1 revision)

How much stress intensity K does the 50 MPa surge value contribute?

How would you reassess your design's reserve factor in the light of this new information on loading?

The extra 6 MPa √m of crack driver produced by the surge is part of the normal operating cycle so needs to be added to the K values due to operating pressure and residual stresses, giving:

$$K_{operating} = K_{primary} + K_{residual} + K_{surge}$$
$$\approx 38 \text{ MPa } \sqrt{m} + 13 \text{ MPa } \sqrt{m} + 6 \text{ MPa } \sqrt{m}$$
$$\approx 57 \text{ MPa } \sqrt{m}$$

which creates a reserve of:

$$\frac{140 \text{ MPa } \sqrt{m}}{57 \text{ MPa} \sqrt{m}} \approx 2.5$$

My emergency shutdown design gives:

$$K_{emergency} = K_{primary} + K_{residual} + K_{thermal}$$
$$\approx 38 \text{ MPa } \sqrt{m} + 13 \text{ MPa } \sqrt{m} + 15 \text{ MPa } \sqrt{m}$$
$$\approx 66 \text{ MPa } \sqrt{m}$$

which creates a reserve of:

$$\frac{140 \text{ MPa } \sqrt{m}}{66 \text{ MPa } \sqrt{m}} \approx 2.1$$

You now have the plant working at its normal design conditions. There may be a crack 3 mm in length that, because you are a conservative engineer, you assume is oriented in the most dangerous direction under a K crack-driving parameter during normal service of $K_{operating} = 57$ MPa √m.

The question of how fast the crack grows under a cyclic loading of 100 MPa occurring some 10 times a day now presents itself – cue the Paris law. First, though, I have to find the crack length at which brittle failure takes place. Reflect on this problem for a moment; it is not straightforward.

The difficulty is that the primary and residual stresses are tensile and so use the same Y calibration curve (so one can add the stresses); but the thermal shock stresses are in bending and so use a different Y calibration curve. There is no fundamental problem in this: just use the calculator, keep increasing the crack length in increments and calculating the value of $K_{emergency}$ until it equals the material toughness of 140 MPa √m.

This is a little tedious, but I can use conservatism to make life simpler. The thermal shock stresses in bending generate less K than if they were in tension (if you remember this from Part 1, fine; if you don't, then have a play with the K calculator to prove it to yourself). So, if I do this the easy way, using tension for all the components of K, and the result is that design analysis is satisfactory, then I needn't go any further; this saves me time and money.

SAQ 2.7 (Learning outcomes 2.6 and 2.7)

(a) Use the K calculator to find what the critical crack length is for the emergency shutdown procedure, assuming that the thermal shock stresses create a tensile field.

(b) Using your answer to (a), use the Fatigue calculator to find the number of cycles it takes to grow the crack from 3 mm to failure in order to recommend an inspection procedure. If the plant cycles 10 times per day, what is its total lifetime?

(c) The crack is subjected to 10 load cycles per day. Estimate how much the crack will grow in 2 years. (The calculator won't allow a direct calculation of this, but input values of final crack length until you obtain 2 years' worth of cycles.)

I am beginning to like this design! A recommendation for crack detection after 2 years will do as a starter. If no cracks are detected, then the inspection period can probably be increased progressively.

How critical are the values of the initial and final flaw sizes to our calculations? The answer to this can depend on just how much difference there is between the initial and final lengths. In this example, the final crack length is about twice the starting flaw size, which is quite a small difference. If the crack has further to grow, because more cycles are required to grow it when it is small (because ΔK is smaller), then the final crack length is less important. Figure 2.50 shows this effect, where large changes in a_f result in small changes in N_f.

Knowing the initial flaw size is critically important. Without knowing the likely flaw distribution, or being able to measure for flaws accurately, damage-tolerance analysis is either speculative or is forced to be overconservative. It is also difficult to apply damage tolerance to parts (for example, in the F-111) where a relatively small crack extension from a flaw can lead to failure; indeed, there are additional complicating factors associated with the behaviour of ☑ **small cracks** ☑ that are a particular concern within fatigue analysis. ☑ **Trouble on the runway** ☑ gives a recent example of where experience in service has led to a change in inspection and maintenance for a safety-critical component.

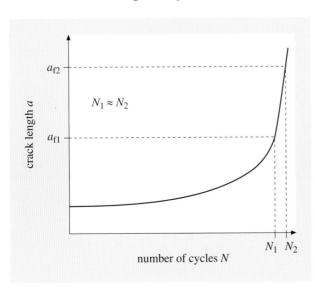

Figure 2.50 Effect of crack size on the fatigue life

☑ Small cracks

The crack propagation data, like the da/dN versus ΔK plots in Figures 2.40 and 2.42, are conventionally obtained using laboratory tests on standard test-pieces, e.g. compact-tension specimens. The procedure in these tests involves growing a fatigue crack away from a starter notch, typically by 1–5 mm, before recording the propagation rate under a constant stress range and ratio. The data obtained for shorter crack lengths are not suitable owing to the stress concentration effect of the notch where the crack begins, and where there may also be some plastic strain. Remember from Part 1 that in calculating the stress intensity the *far-field* stress is used, with no assumption of a stress concentration at the crack tip. So, until they grow out of the stress field of the notch, reaching to the bulk stress field of the specimen, small cracks, especially shorter than a millimetre, grow

much faster than expected on the basis of nominal ΔK values, as seen in Figure 2.51. They may even grow at speeds below the threshold value predicted by LEFM. This is primarily due to the failure of LEFM to characterize the crack-driving force in a region with relatively high plasticity. A significant contribution to the difference is believed to be due to crack closure, or more accurately the lack of it, because of the undeveloped crack wake (see the input 'Crack closure') with the small cracks. Reduced crack closure produces a larger ΔK_{eff} and, hence, results in a higher crack-growth rate.

It is also possible for non-propagating fatigue cracks to form at notches, where a crack initiates, grows and then stops, even if the magnitude of the applied load cycle does not change. As the stress concentration effect of the notch decreases with

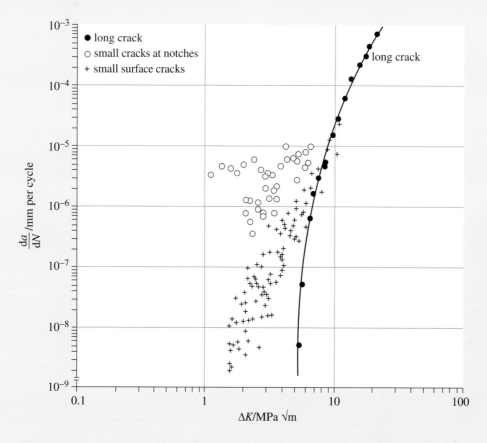

Figure 2.51   Small cracks grow faster than predicted by 'long' crack data

distance from the root of the notch, the magnitude of the stress field at the crack tip may decrease as the crack propagates; and if the remote stress is sufficiently low, the crack may stop altogether within the notch-affected zone.

The small-crack effect is an example of where similitude clearly fails. That is, the stress pattern ahead of a short crack within a notch field is different from that for longer cracks outside the notch stress field. Such small cracks are referred to as 'mechanically short cracks'.

The anomalous behaviour of fatigue cracks at short lengths is not just restricted to notches or stress concentrations. Any newly initiated small crack will at some point be comparable in size to the microstructural dimensions (such as the sizes of grains or strengthening particles) in engineering alloys. Microstructural features such as grain boundaries and second-phase particles can act as effective barriers to crack propagation. As such, they may alter the stress field around the crack tip in various ways, and hence affect the crack propagation rates.

For example, the crack path may deviate from the direction perpendicular to the direction of maximum principal stress and follow structurally weaker paths. Take a look at the path of the small crack in the unnotched specimen, made of an aluminium alloy, shown in Figure 2.52. The crack, which had propagated through a grain (grain A), changes its path when it reaches the grain boundary. Rather than crossing the boundary and propagating in the same direction in the neighbouring grain, propagates along the grain boundary. It seems that the crystallographic orientation of the next grain (grain B) is less favourable to crack propagation than grain A. Since the crack is now propagating at an inclined angle to the direction of maximum principal stress, the crack tip experiences a somewhat lessened stress field and would slow down. At the next junction along the grain boundary, the crack has to choose another favourable path. It seems that the crystallographic convenience of grain C was less than that of the grain boundary, which the crack eventually chose. Even more deviation from the usual direction meant that this crack-growth rate most probably had to fall considerably – growth may even have stopped altogether.

Another example is shown in Figure 2.53, where a crack was stopped several times at microstructural barriers (at particles indicated by the points A–E), before 're-initiating' and continuing to grow. This sort of behaviour does, in fact, provide a clue as to why some alloys exhibit a fatigue limit and some don't.

If the microstructure of the material contains 'natural' crack stoppers, like the iron–iron carbide laths of pearlite in steels (Figure 2.54), then small cracks can be arrested long before they can grow to

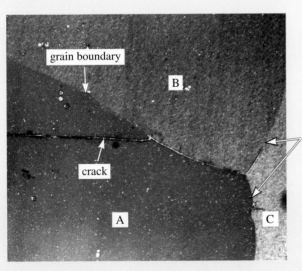

Figure 2.52   The path of a small crack in an aluminium alloy specimen

a critical length for propagation. This is the origin of the fatigue limit in many steels, which I introduced earlier. But note that the fatigue limit effect can be negated is a single overload causes the crack to break through a barrier and begin to grow anew.

There are very serious practical implications for the small-crack problem. Since most fatigue-life prediction methods rely on long-crack data, and as overall life is most influenced by low propagation rate behaviour, the accelerated and 'sub-threshold'

(a)

(b)

(c)

Figure 2.53 Arresting of a crack at microstructural barriers in an aluminium alloy: (a) micrograph of the crack taken using a scanning electron microscope; (b) sketch of the crack; (c) the corresponding crack-growth rate in the microstructure extension of small cracks can lead to potentially dangerous overpredictions of fatigue life.

Fortunately, new techniques are implementing some aspects of small-crack behaviour into fatigue-life prediction models that have been emerging recently. For example, it is viable to predict the behaviour of mechanically short cracks at stress raisers on the basis of crack closure measurements, and/or correlate the crack propagation rate using parameters that allow some plasticity. Modelling 'microstructurally small cracks' is proving to be more difficult, though. The complex interaction of cracks with microstructure has been only partially successful using complex statistical models.

Better understanding of the behaviour of small cracks will lead to less conservative designs, which will mean lighter and more efficient (using less fuel, so more environmentally friendly) aircraft.

Figure 2.54   Pearlite in steel

✉ Trouble on the runway

On 2 June 2006, a ground test was being performed on an American Airlines Boeing 767 fitted with General Electric engines. The flight crew had reported a power lag in the left engine on its previous flight. The ground crew had powered the engines to maximum twice when there was an explosion in the left engine. The high-pressure turbine stage 1 disc had ruptured, with large pieces of debris being thrown out of the engine housing. One piece bounced off the runway, through the aircraft fuselage and lodged in the engine cowling on the other side of the plane (Figure 2.55). Another fragment was found over 700 m away against an airport perimeter fence; it had crossed two active runways and taxiways to get there! The engine was a total loss, and the plane was damaged substantially. Fortunately, there were no injuries.

Post-incident metallurgical examination revealed that the disk rupture was the result of a radial fracture that originated at a small dent found at the bottom of a blade slot. You will recall from Block 1 that the blade roots in turbine discs are sources of stress concentration. Defects introduced during fabrication or maintenance can make things worse in such highly stressed areas of a component. The examination also revealed two other similar cracks on the disk. The disk had accumulated 9186 flight cycles in service (48 429 h), and had 5814 cycles remaining before compulsory retirement at its design limit of 15 000 cycles.

Clearly, if this failure had happened in flight the aircraft could have crashed, though other such failures in the past have not always had disastrous consequences.

The consequences of the incident were that enhanced inspection regimes were instigated for the engine type concerned, particularly for discs that had previously had repair work in the blade root. All discs that had accumulated more than 3000 cycles required immediate inspection and reworking of the blade root if it had not already been performed. The entire design of the disc was also reviewed to ensure future safety.

Figure 2.55   Part of No. 1 engine lodged in No. 2 after bouncing off the runway

4.4 Linking initiation and propagation

For a fracture mechanics analysis, we must always assume a realistic initial flaw size. If we let the initial crack length shrink to zero, we are faced with a problem: the propagation life tends to infinity, irrespective of stress range, because the initial $\Delta K = 0$! How can we overcome this difficulty?

The mathematical reason for our dilemma is, of course, that if $a = 0$, then $\Delta K = 0$ and the growth rate is zero. The Paris equation is *only valid for Stage II growth,* but initiation and early growth is a Stage I shear-controlled process. Thus, the techniques of fracture mechanics *cannot be applied directly to the initiation phase.* If we want to calculate the total fatigue life, then we will have to split our calculation into two parts. The first stage lumps together initiation and early growth to a crack length a_0; the second calculates the crack growth from a_0 to failure.

Unfortunately, no quantitative theories of initiation exist, so again it is necessary to fall back on an empirical or experimental approach. Test data can be collected under strain-cycling conditions. The number of cycles to initiate and grow a small crack, typically and arbitrarily 0.5 mm long, can be plotted against the applied strain range, as shown in Figure 2.56. The amount of growth depends on the sensitivity of the measurement technique used. Note that this is a strain-cycles curve for *initiation*, not failure.

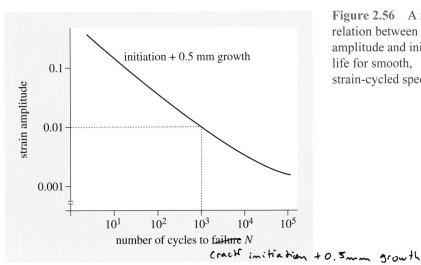

Figure 2.56 A measured relation between strain amplitude and initiation life for smooth, strain-cycled specimens

These data can now be used to calculate the initiation life of a component, if we know the strain range at the site of crack initiation. As an example, if we determine that the strain amplitude at the notch root is 0.01, then we can consult Figure 2.56 to find that this corresponds to an initiation life of 10^3 cycles. We can then use the Paris law to calculate the propagation life in the elastic region away from the notch root.

SAQ 2.8 (Learning outcomes 2.2 and 2.6)

If $a_f = 100$ mm, $\sigma_a = 80$ MPa, $Y = 1.2$ and $C = 10^{-11}$, what is the propagation life if the initial crack length is 0.5 mm?

Hint: use Equation (2.19).

Thus, the total life by this two-stage process is given by:

N_f = initiation cycles and propagation cycles

≈ 1000 cycles + 15 000 cycles

$\approx 16\,000$ cycles

This simplified example, therefore, illustrates how we might link the initiation and propagation stages to calculate the total fatigue life.

SAQ 2.9 (Learning outcomes 2.2 and 2.8)

For a typical steel alloy subjected to an alternating stress of amplitude 100 MPa, what is the maximum length of a centre crack in a large plate that would just fail to grow by fatigue? The fatigue threshold has been measured as 6 MPa √m.

One approach that attempts to look at fatigue safety in terms of stress and crack length is ☑ **the Kitagawa–Takahashi method** ☑.

☑ The Kitagawa–Takahashi method

This approach is best illustrated diagrammatically: see Figure 2.57.

The y-axis is the threshold stress for crack propagation; the x-axis is the length of any existing crack in the material.

At small crack lengths, typically 1 μm or less, the threshold stress is simply the fatigue limit of the material. At longer crack lengths, typically greater than 1 mm, the threshold stress is derived from the Paris equation, using the threshold stress-intensity range ΔK_{th}, below which cracks do not propagate.

Where these two extremes of behaviour intersect is the value of the crack length l_0, which is a critical crack size below which any cracks present do not affect the fatigue limit. This is in line with the concept of small cracks that can be arrested by local microstructural features.

The curved line in between the two extremes is found to fit experimental data reasonably well.

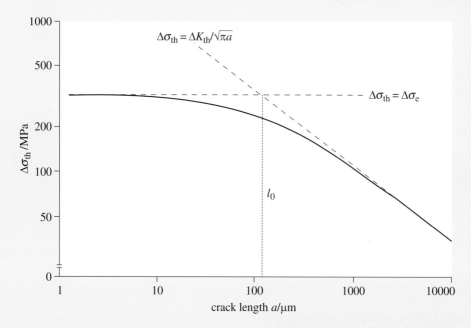

Figure 2.57   Kitagawa–Takahashi diagram for a nodular cast iron; $\Delta\sigma_e$ = 320 MPa, ΔK_{th} = 6.2 measured at R = 0.1

5 A PRACTICAL EXAMPLE: THE MARKHAM DISASTER

The plan view of the fracture surface of a broken brake rod from a mineshaft lift is shown in Figure 2.58. Its failure cased the death of 14 miners at the Markham colliery in July 1973. The rod had been installed 21 years earlier. Following the accident, an extensive investigation took place to identify the cause of failure.

The rod is simply a long threaded bar, 51.3 mm in diameter with a 3.34 mm deep thread.

Detailed stress analysis found that the axial stress in the threaded portion of the brake rod was 97 MPa. Tests on the steel showed that its yield and tensile strengths were 346 MPa and 600 MPa respectively.

EXERCISE 2.10

What factor of safety does the axial stress represent in respect of the yield strength and the tensile strength? Does this suggest that the load was sufficient to cause failure by static loading?

So the axial stress on its own was too low to cause failure of the brake rod. But further examination of the assembly revealed that a bearing designed to keep the brake rod axially aligned had, through lack of maintenance, seized and was creating a bending moment on the rod. Further stress analysis (using strain gauges on an operating assembly) revealed that the bending stress on the rod was 157 MPa. This, combined with the axial stress, gives a total stress of 254 MPa. This is much higher, but still well within the material's yield strength.

Figure 2.58 The plan view of the fracture surface of a broken brake rod

The investigators then turned to fatigue as the possible cause. Owing to the on/off cyclic nature of the brake rod and because of the way the brake operated, there was always an applied stress on the rod even when the brake was off. It was established that the total cyclic load was 211 MPa (a combination of the axial and bending stresses) and the mean stress was 129 MPa.

SAQ 2.10 (Learning outcomes 2.2 and 2.4)

The closest data that were found for this type of steel gave a tensile strength of 540 MPa and a reverse bending fatigue limit of ±120 MPa.
Using the Goodman relation (either by drawing a diagram or using the equation), establish whether these cyclic stresses would be high enough to cause failure by fatigue.

So, using the Goodman diagram we find that fatigue will occur as a result of the combined bending and tensile stresses. We could stop here and say: 'Well, what do you expect?' The stresses say that it would fail by fatigue, and the fracture surface is consistent with this.

However, to be sure, it would be sensible to confirm that the expected crack-growth rates in the material, and the anticipated load cycling, would lead to the lifetime that was observed in reality.

The brake would have been cycled each time the mine lift was used. An estimation of the number of cycles experienced, given the average daily use of the lift, was 3×10^5 cycles.

SAQ 2.11 (Learning outcomes 2.2 and 2.6)

Using the cyclic stress established earlier, calculate the number of cycles to failure; assume that the initial crack length was 0.1 mm and the final crack length was 29 mm. For this particular steel, take $C = 10^{-11}$ and $m = 3$.

Hint: the geometry does not fit exactly with those in the fatigue calculator, but you should use 'beam in pure bending' geometry.

Although the figure calculated in SAQ 2.11 is very much an estimate (because of the geometry chosen it is more likely to be on the conservative side), it is still in fairly good agreement with the actual number of cycles prior to failure. So everything stacks up: the bending load on the shaft led to fatigue failure pretty much exactly when it would have been predicted had all the factors been known in advance. This is often the case with fatigue failures.

If the applied stress was due only to the axial loading, as the design was intended, then the fatigue life expectancy would have approached an infinite life! The final outcome of the investigation found that the ultimate cause of failure was the ineffective bearing that led to bending of the brake rod, and recommendations were that, in addition to improved design of the bearing, the system should operate in a fail-safe manner.

6 SUMMARY: FATIGUE DESIGN

Hopefully, you are now in a better position to comprehend the difficulties facing the designer who has to tackle situations that involve cyclic loading. It should be evident from studying this part that design against failure by fatigue is far more complex than design against failure by static loading.

Although fatigue can be well characterized by a material's S–N behaviour or the growth rate of a fatigue crack as a result of cyclic loading, it can be challenging to account for safely. Fatigue lives are affected by chemical environments, including air and water vapour, and are sensitive to the surface condition.

It is surprising how frequently fatigue failures are caused simply by poor detailing, e.g. by the use of inadequate radii of curvature at changes of section. Anything that might cause a stress concentration can act as a fatigue initiation point. Fatigue design, in just the same way as designing for strength, is a compromise between the cost and weight of a component and its performance in service. Aircraft that were designed to be entirely fatigue-free would be too heavy to leave the ground.

The successful design of a component or structure reflects a judicious and, where possible, rigorous stress analysis, coupled with due care and attention to the choice of material and control of its microstructure and the selection of an appropriate surface condition for the component. Due regard must also be given to the environment in which the component will operate. Further, the designer must be careful to allow for the statistical scatter associated with fatigue test data and must remember that there is a specimen-size effect in fatigue. Also, the designer must appreciate the need for regular inspection of a critical component when it is in service.

Along with the other failure modes considered in this course, fatigue provides a further example of the need for inputs from both the design engineer and the metallurgist or materials engineer.

LEARNING OUTCOMES

After studying Block 2 Part 2 you should be able to do the following.

2.1 Describe the origin of a fatigue failure, given appropriate information, in terms of a design flaw or other operational problem.

2.2 Perform simple fatigue calculations, given appropriate data.

2.3 Describe the effect of a notch or stress concentrator in fatigue initiation, and describe the effect of notch sensitivity.

2.4 Use the Goodman relation to predict the effect of changes in mean stress on the fatigue limit or fatigue life of a material.

2.5 Describe the applications of 'cycle-counting' methods, such as Miner's rule, in assessing the lifetimes of components subjected to complex loading.

2.6 Use the Paris law to calculate the growth rate of a fatigue crack.

2.7 Use the Fatigue calculator spreadsheet to assess lifetimes of growing cracks.

2.8 Describe and apply the concept of a fatigue threshold, below which cracks do not propagate.

ANSWERS TO EXERCISES

EXERCISE 2.1

In Part 1 you learnt that cracks should not cause failure unless the stress intensity at the crack tip exceeds the material's fracture toughness. Clearly, this isn't what happens in fatigue; somehow the crack is growing because of the cyclic nature of the loading, even though the maximum stress intensity is below K_{IC}. This is what makes fatigue so dangerous.

EXERCISE 2.2

(a) The maximum stress is $+\sigma_a$ and the minimum stress is $-\sigma_a$.
    Therefore, $R = -\sigma_a/\sigma_a = -1$.

(b) The maximum stress is 200 MPa and the minimum stress is 40 MPa.
    Therefore, $R = 40/200 = 0.2$.

(c) The maximum stress is 300 MPa and the minimum stress is 0 MPa.
    Therefore, $R = 0/300 = 0$.

(d) The maximum stress is 200 MPa and the minimum stress is −20 MPa.
    Therefore, $R = -20/200 = -0.1$.

EXERCISE 2.3

(a) At 1 Hz the machine will take 2×10^9 s, i.e. over 63 years!

(b) At 100 Hz the test would take just over 231 days.

So, establishing the fatigue properties precisely at long lives can be very time consuming.

EXERCISE 2.4

Using Figure 2.21:

(a) From the line that is parallel to the x-axis the fatigue limit is about 340 MPa.

(b) Reading from the graph it is about 120 MPa.

EXERCISE 2.5

(a) In push–pull testing, the whole specimen section is subjected to the maximum stress cycle. In the bend test, only the surface layers farthest from the neutral axis experience the peak stress.

(b) The larger volume of highly stressed material in the push–pull test is statistically more likely to contain a flaw, so failure tends to occur earlier in the axial test.

EXERCISE 2.6

The strength of a material tends to decrease with temperature (and conversely the toughness increases). Because the fatigue limit changes with the strength of the material, lowering the strength will increase the susceptibility to fatigue.

EXERCISE 2.7

Using Goodman:

$$\sigma_a = \sigma_{a0}\left(1 - \frac{\sigma_m}{\sigma_t}\right)$$

$$\sigma_{a,100} = 200 \text{ MPa} \times \left(1 - \frac{100 \text{ MPa}}{500 \text{ MPa}}\right)$$

$$= 160 \text{ MPa}$$

Therefore, $\sigma_{a,100} = 160$ MPa.

EXERCISE 2.8

0.05 mm increments produced 30 248 cycles, 100 increments (0.005 mm) produced 31 368 cycles, 1000 increments (0.0005 mm) produced 31 358 cycles. Therefore, choosing too coarse an increment of growth will produce a non-conservative result: one that is too low.

EXERCISE 2.9

It takes 8334 cycles to grow the crack from 3 mm to 3.2 mm (Figure 2.59) and 4523 cycles to grow it from 3.8 mm to 4 mm (Figure 2.60) at a increment of 0.005 mm.

Figure 2.59 Plate in tension with a through-thickness edge crack: 8334 cycles to grow the crack from 3.0 mm to 3.2 mm at an increment of 0.005 mm

EXERCISE 2.10

Against the yield stress, the factor of safety is 346/97 = 3.6.

Against the tensile strength it is 600/97 = 6.2.

So failure by the static load seems unlikely.

Figure 2.60   Plate in tension with a through-thickness edge crack: 4523 cycles to grow the crack from 3.8 mm to 4.0 mm at an increment of 0.005 mm

ANSWERS TO SELF-ASSESSMENT QUESTIONS

SAQ 2.1

(a) The Comet failed because of various stress concentrators in the structure that could initiate fatigue cracking under cyclic loading. Initial fatigue testing of the structure had not revealed the problem because it had not been undertaken under the same conditions that a real fuselage structure would experience.

(b) The *Alexander L. Kielland* platform collapsed after a fatigue crack grew from a hydrophone mounting. The weld securing the hydrophone was of poor quality, and a crack grew from the weld, eventually fracturing the brace to which it was attached. Poor design then led, through a series of failures of other connecting structures, to the capsizing of the platform.

(c) The cause of Eschede train crash can be traced to the design of wheel used. The original monoblock design was changed to a design using a separate tyre on the central wheel, with a rubber insert to reduce noise. Unfortunately, the external tyre could then flex in bending, particularly as its thickness reduced by wear. A fatigue crack grew from the inner tyre surface and caused the failure of the wheel.

SAQ 2.2

From the data in Table 2.1, the fatigue limit of unnotched samples is 232 MPa ($\alpha_k = 1$); the value for notched samples varies with the sharpness of the notch, i.e. with α_k.

For $\alpha_k = 3.02$, the fatigue limit is 108 MPa, thus:

$$\alpha_f = 232/108 = 2.15$$

and

$$q = \frac{(232/108) - 1}{3.02 - 1} = 0.57$$

Values of α_f and q can be determined in the same way for each α_k given; the results appear in Table 2.4. The values of q vary depending on the stress concentration values, but they all indicate that the material is notch-sensitive.

Table 2.4 Values of fatigue notch factor α_f and the notch sensitivity factor q for the values of a_k given in Table 2.1

α_k	σ_{FL}	α_f	q
1	232	–	–
1.84	137	232/137 = 1.69	0.82
2.26	120	232/120 = 1.93	0.74
3.02	108	232/108 = 2.15	0.57
4.6	86	232/86 = 2.70	0.47
7.06	91	232/91 = 2.55	0.26

SAQ 2.3

Using Goodman:

$$\sigma_{a,200} = \sigma_{a0}\left(1 - \frac{\sigma_m}{\sigma_t}\right)$$

$$120\ \text{MPa} = \sigma_{a0}\left(1 - \frac{200}{420}\right)\text{MPa}$$

$$\sigma_{a0} = \frac{120\ \text{MPa}}{0.52} = 231\ \text{MPa}$$

SAQ 2.4

Substituting these values into Equation (2.19) gives:

$$N_f = \frac{1}{C\left(Y2\sigma_a\right)^4 \pi^2 a_i}\left\{1 - \frac{a_i}{a_f}\right\}$$

$$= \frac{1}{10^{-11}\times\left(1.2\times80\right)^4 \times \pi^2 \times 0.004}\times\left(1 - 0.5\right)$$

$$\approx 15\ 000\ \text{cycles}$$

Therefore, the number of cycles to failure will be approximately 15 000.

SAQ 2.5

Using the calculator gives $K_{primary} \approx 38$ MPa $\sqrt{m}$ (Figure 2.61), $K_{residual} \approx 13$ MPa $\sqrt{m}$ (Figure 2.62) and $K_{thermal} \approx 15$ MPa $\sqrt{m}$ (Figure 2.63), giving a total crack-driving parameter of:

$$K_{emergency} \approx \left(38 + 13 + 15\right)\ \text{MPa}\ \sqrt{m} \approx 66\ \text{MPa}\ \sqrt{m}$$

Figure 2.61 Plate in tension with a through-thickness edge crack $-K_{primary} \approx 38$ MPa √m

Figure 2.62 Plate in tension with a through-thickness edge crack $-K_{residual} \approx 13$ MPa √m

Material properties:

K_{IC}: [   ] MPa √m

Geometry dimensions:
Width (W): 18.000 mm
Crack length (a): 3.000 mm
Y: 1.30

Loading:
Stress: 100.00 MPa
K_I: 12.60 MPa √m
Reserve factor on the load: 0.00

Figure 2.63 Plate in pure bending with a through-thickness edge crack $-K_{thermal} \approx 15$ MPa √m

Beam in pure bending - through-thickness edge crack

Calculate: ● KI
○ Critical crack length
○ Critical stress
○ KIC

Material properties:

K_{IC}: [   ] MPa √m

Geometry dimensions:
Width (W): 18.000 mm
Crack length (a): 3.000 mm
Y: 1.05

Loading:
Stress: 150.00 MPa
K_I: 15.22 MPa √m
Reserve factor on the load: 0.00

The toughness of the steel is 140 MPa √m, so the reserve factor on load is
140 MPa √m/66 MPa √m ≈ 2.1.

SAQ 2.6

Another 50 MPa worth of K in terms of crack driving would contribute 6 MPa √m to
the K-driving parameter (Figure 2.64).

Do I add this on to the existing K values, giving a total of $66 + 6 ≈ 72$ MPa √m and
so reducing the reserve to 140 MPa √m/72 MPa √m ≈ 1.9 on emergency shutdown?
I think not: this is a surge on start-up, which is part of the normal cycle of use;
if I were to sum the start-up surge K and the emergency shutdown K, I would be
assuming that start-up and shutdown could hit peak conditions simultaneously. I
think this is incredible, so I choose not to do it.

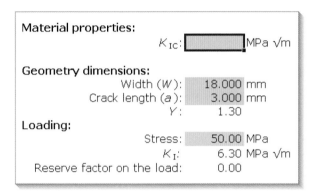

Figure 2.64 Plate in tension with a through-thickness edge
crack – $K_I ≈ 6$ MPa √m

But note that in the nuclear industry there is a 'condition of incredibility' that
demands you use anything possible, no matter how incredible.

So, if you have factored for the surge on the grounds of conservatism that is fine by
me – there are no correct answers in this game. You just have to be able to justify
your approach to your boss, regulator, conscience or God!

SAQ 2.7

(a) I have a design primary stress of 300 MPa, a thermal shock stress of 150 MPa
    and a secondary residual stress of 100 MPa, giving a total of 550 MPa, all in
    tension. The K calculator produces a critical crack length of about 6.2 mm
    (Figure 2.65).
(b) The Fatigue calculator produces about 64 000 cycles, (Figure 2.66), which if
    cycling at 10 times a day means that it will be about 17 years before the crack
    grows long enough to fail under emergency shutdown conditions. There is no
    point in refining this analysis, as we clearly have plenty of time to play with and
    no immediate cause for concern.
(c) Two years is some 7300 cycles. The Fatigue calculator does not allow a direct
    calculation, but it is easy enough to try a few values of final crack length until
    about 7300 cycles are returned. I get a crack length of about 3.2 mm, which is
    just long enough to move into the detectable zone for non-destructive testing.

Figure 2.65   Plate in tension with a through-thickness edge crack – critical crack length ≈ 6.2 mm

Figure 2.66   Plate in tension with a through-thickness edge crack – number of cycles = 64 119

SAQ 2.8

There is a little trick here to make the calculation easier. As $a_f \gg a_i$, $(1 - a_i/a_f)$ is 0.995, i.e. close to unity, so we can reduce Equation (2.19) to:

$$N_f = \frac{1}{C\left(Y2\sigma_a\right)^4 \pi^2 a_i}$$

Substituting the values given and taking $a_i = 0.5$ mm we get $N_f \approx 15\ 000$ cycles.

SAQ 2.9

The crack will not grow if the applied stress-intensity range ΔK is less than the threshold value ΔK_{th}. For a centre crack in a large plate, $Y = 1$, and in this case $\Delta \sigma = 200$ MPa and $\Delta K_{th} = 6$ MPa $\sqrt{m}$. So, using $\Delta K = Y \Delta \sigma \sqrt{\pi a}$:

$$\sqrt{\pi a_0} = \frac{\Delta K_{th}}{\Delta \sigma} = 0.03\ \sqrt{m}$$

Therefore:

$$a_0 = 0.29\ \text{mm}$$

where a_0 is the length of the largest crack that would just fail to grow.

SAQ 2.10

I have plotted a Goodman diagram using this data in Figure 2.67. The straight line joins a point on the y-axis corresponding to the fatigue limit and a point on the x-axis corresponding to the tensile strength. I have also plotted the point with the value of $\Delta\sigma/2$ and σ_m corresponding to the conditions within the threaded region of the rod. The point lies above the Goodman line, and so I conclude that fatigue at the root of the threads is likely.

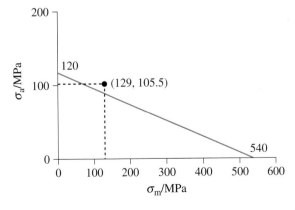

Figure 2.67   Goodman diagram for the answer to SAQ 2.9

SAQ 2.11

Using 211 MPa as the load range and the values given, the number of cycles should calculate as 2.50×10^5 when using a growth increment of 0.05 mm and 2.64×10^5 when using an increment of 0.01 mm.

REFERENCES

Civil Aeronautics Board (March 1956) Airplane Airworthiness Transport Categories, Part 4b-3, para 270.

Fairbairn, W. (1864) 'Experiments to determine the effect of impact, vibratory action, and long-continued changes of load on wrought-iron girders', *Philosophical Transactions of the Royal Society of London*, vol. 154, pp. 311–25.

Suresh, S. and Ritchie, R. O. (1982) 'A geometric model for fatigue crack closure induced by fracture surface roughness', *Metallurgical and Materials Transactions A*, vol. 13A, pp. 1627–1631.

ACKNOWLEDGEMENTS

Grateful acknowledgement is made to the following sources:

FIGURES

Figure 2.4: © The Flight Collection/Alamy.

Figure 2.8(a): © STR/AP/EMPICS.

Figure 2.8(c): Maier G. (ed) (1985) Case Histories in Offshore Engineering, CISM.

Figure 2.9: © Alex Grimm/Reuters/Corbis.

Figure 2.11: © Getty Images.

Figure 2.16: © Peter Menzel/Science Photo Library.

Figure 2.18: Courtesy of Cranfield University.

Figure 2.19: Courtesy of Dr Sarah Hainsworth, University of Leicester.

Figure 2.26: Electro General Corporation for D.F. Socie, Fatigue Life Estimation Techniques, Technical Report, No. 145.

Figure 2.28: McGraw Hill (1967) for A.T. Benedetto, 'The Structure & Properties of Materials'.

Figure 2.33(a): Photograph taken from Accident Investigation Report 9/78, Boeing 707 321C G-BEBP. Department of Trade Accidents Investigation Branch © Crown copyright. Reproduced with the permission of the Controller of HMSO and Queen's Printer for Scotland.

Figure 2.33(c): Photograph taken from Accident Investigation Report 9/78, Boeing 707 321C G-BEBP. Department of Trade Accidents Investigation Branch © Crown copyright. Reproduced with the permission of the Controller of HMSO and Queen's Printer for Scotland.

Figure 2.39: © Purestock/Getty Images.

Figures 2.51–3: Courtesy of Dr Salih Gungor, The Open University.

Figure 2.55: Blakey, M.C., (2006) US National Transportation Safety Board, Safety Recommendation Report, 28 August 2006. Taken from http://www.ntsb.gov

COURSE TEAM ACKNOWLEDGEMENTS

This part was prepared for the course team by Jim Moffatt, Adrian Demaid and Michael Fitzpatrick, with contributions by Salih Gungor.

T357 COURSE TEAM

Professor Michael Fitzpatrick (course team chair)

Andy Harding (course manager)

Jackie Burnicle (course manager)

ACADEMIC STAFF

Dr Alun Armstrong

Professor Adrian Demaid

Professor Chris Earl

Professor Lyndon Edwards

Dr Salih Gungor

Michael Hush

Dr Peter Lewis

Dr Jim Moffatt

Dr Ed Murphy

Dr Martin Rist

EXTERNAL ASSESSOR

Professor Lindsay Greer, University of Cambridge

CONSULTANTS

Martin Goldthorpe

David Sefton (critical reader)

Olivier Zanellato (critical reader)

SUPPORT STAFF

Debbie Derbyshire (course team secretary)

Colin Gagg

Stan Hiller

Pete Ledgard

Rehana Malik

PRODUCTION TEAM

Kirsten Barnett

Annette Booz

Philippa Broadbent

Lisa Carrick

Teresa Cox

Sarah Crompton

Daphne Cross

Anna Edgley-Smith

Vicky Eves

Chris French

Carol Houghton

Jonathan Martyn

Katie Meade

Lara Mynors

Deana Plummer

Lynn Short

Susanne Umerski